CW00382341
Puzzler
COLLECTION
100 PAGES
in CASH PRIZES
WIN!
a NINTENDO Wii and GREAT DAYS OUT for a WHOLE YEAR
ADMIT ONE
FREE!
PUZZLER FAVOURITES
THE WORLD'S FAVOURITE PUZZLE MAGAZINE FOR OVER
YEARS!
The Puzzler
Puzzler
COLLECTION
100 PAGES
£2,000 IN CASH
The original and best
Puzzler
No.911 January 2014 • £1.95
100 YEARS OF THE CROSSWORD
WIN THE TRIP OF A LIFETIME TO NEW YORK!
£6,000 in cash prizes!
The Puzzler
Happy New Year
WIN £2000 IN CASH PRIZES INSIDE!

Contents

7 History of Puzzles
8 How to Solve

10 **JANUARY**
11 – 24 Puzzles
12 – 15 Diary
24 – 25 Solutions

26 **FEBRUARY**
27 – 38 Puzzles
28 – 31 Diary
38 – 39 Solutions

40 **MARCH**
41 – 54 Puzzles
42 – 45 Diary
54 – 55 Solutions

56 **APRIL**
57 – 68 Puzzles
58 – 61 Diary
68 – 69 Solutions

70 **MAY**
71 – 84 Puzzles
72 – 75 Diary
84 – 85 Solutions

86 **JUNE**
87 – 98 Puzzles
88 – 91 Diary
98 – 99 Solutions

100 **JULY**
101 – 114 Puzzles
102 – 105 Diary
114 – 115 Solutions

116 **AUGUST**
117 – 128 Puzzles
118 – 121 Diary
128 – 129 Solutions

130 **SEPTEMBER**
131 – 144 Puzzles
132 – 135 Diary
144 – 145 Solutions

146 **OCTOBER**
147 – 158 Puzzles
148 – 151 Diary
158 – 159 Solutions

160 **NOVEMBER**
161 – 174 Puzzles
162 – 165 Diary
174 – 175 Solutions

176 **DECEMBER**
177 – 186 Puzzles
178 – 181 Diary
186 – 187 Solutions

A year with

Name
Address
Postcode
Home Phone
Mobile Phone
Email

In case of emergency, contact:

Name
Telephone

Welcome

Puzzler

Hello and welcome to the Puzzler Yearbook 2015 - a perfect way to enjoy your favourite puzzles from the magazines every day of the year, plus the added value of a diary for each week to make it even more useful.

The name Puzzler is synonymous with great puzzles. Puzzler is the oldest and best known of all puzzle magazines, and the company is known for its puzzle expertise. As the largest puzzle publisher in the UK, and probably the world, Puzzler Media now publishes sixty titles in more than twenty countries.

We have compiled a brilliant selection of the most popular puzzles, including wordsearches, arrowords, crosswords, sudoku and codewords amongst many others.

We hope you will find our yearbook entertaining throughout the year, keeping your brain sharp and your mind busy.

Wishing you a very happy 2015!

From all at Puzzler

Editorial Team:
Jenny Moxham, Becky Crayden, Emma Stacey, Alison Pitcher, David Norris, Heather Allen, Win Magyar

Design:
Julia Toop, Rupal Mistry, Stuart Neil

Puzzler Media, Stonecroft, 69 Station Road, Redhill, Surrey RH1 1EY

www.puzzler.com

Puzzle History

Word puzzles have always been popular – examples of word, or magic squares were pulled from the ruins of Pompeii, having lain buried since 79AD. But crosswords as we know them today have only been around for a century.

In 1913 Arthur Wynne, a Liverpudlian who had emigrated to the USA, was working as the editor of the Fun supplement of the *New York World* Sunday newspaper. Charged with finding a new puzzle to entertain readers in the Christmas edition, he recalled the word squares from his childhood back in 19th-century England. Playing around with the idea, he eventually succeeded in arranging words into a regular diamond shape. He called the puzzle a word-cross and it appeared in the newspaper on December 21.

Wynne's first effort was not a particularly brilliant crossword by today's standards – the answer DOVE appeared twice and there were some very obscure words as answers, such as NARD, NEIF, SERE and TANE.

NARD and SERE are in the *Oxford English Dictionary*, but hardly well known. NEIF and TANE, although clued correctly, are alternative spellings of the Scottish dialect words nieve and tone (or t'one, as opposed to t'other), so would no more have been familiar to the readers of the *New York World* than they will be to you today.

One or two of Wynne's clues were rather vague, such as 'What we all should be' and 'What this puzzle is'. One clue, 'To sink in mud', was couched in the wrong grammatical form. But let's not be too churlish. Most of Wynne's answers still crop up regularly in puzzles today and his word-cross puzzle sure was something new.

The First Crossword

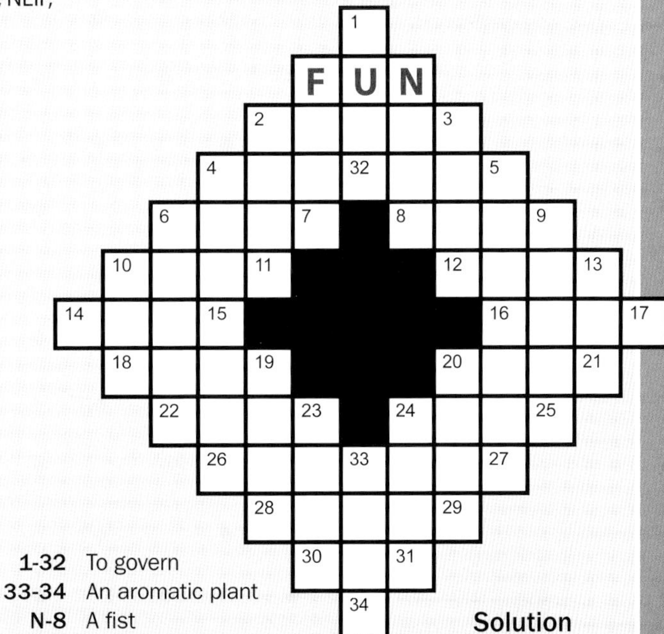

CLUES

2-3 What bargain hunters enjoy
4-5 A written acknowledgment
6-7 Such and nothing more
10-11 A bird
14-15 Opposed to less
18-19 What this puzzle is
22-23 An animal of prey
26-27 The close of a day
28-29 To elude
30-31 The plural of is
8-9 To cultivate
12-13 A bar of wood or iron
16-17 What artists learn to do
20-21 Fastened
24-25 Found on the seashore
10-18 The fibre of the gomuti palm
6-22 What we all should be
4-26 A day dream
2-11 A talon
19-28 A pigeon
F-7 Part of your head
23-30 A river in Russia
1-32 To govern
33-34 An aromatic plant
N-8 A fist
24-31 To agree with
3-12 Part of a ship
20-29 One
5-27 Exchanging
9-25 To sink in mud
13-21 A boy

Solution

How to solve

Here are instructions on how to solve the puzzles that appear most frequently in the Yearbook. Any other variations will have their own introductions.

SUKO

Place the numbers 1-9 in the spaces so that the number in each circle is equal to the sum of the four surrounding spaces and each regional total is correct.

SUDOKU

It is often said that the beauty of Sudoku lies in the fact that there is only one rule: place a digit from 1 to 9 in each empty cell so that each row, each column and each 3x3 block contains all of the digits from 1 to 9.

NUMBER JIG/JIGWORD

A Kriss Kross with numbers or letters. As with a kriss kross, a good place to start solving the puzzle is with those number-lengths that appear the least frequently. Filling the grid is a process of logic, often involving thinking ahead several moves to deduce which of several possible numbers or words is the correct one to fill any given space.

SHORTCODE

Shortcode is an abbreviated form of a Codeword. The objective is the same, to decode the numbers to reveal a Crossword solution. The main difference is that the grid is typically a minuscule 5x5, instead of the usual 15x15. Ten letters have been given a number from 1 to 10. Break the code to complete the Crossword.

LINKWORD

The objective is to find a word of a specific length that can be joined in some way to each of the two clue words to form two new words or phrases. Enter in the grid the four-letter word that comes after the first clue word and before the second clue word to form two new words or phrases. Unscramble the letters in the shaded squares to reveal the mystery word.

BRICKWORK

Enter the answers to the clues in the bricks in the wall. Every word contains the same letters as its neighbour, plus or minus one.

ADD UP

With each number being the sum of the two numbers below it, calculate the top number in the pyramid.

WORD LADDER

The objective is to change one word into another in a series of steps, changing one letter at a time (without rearranging the order of the letters) so that each step is a word.

SUGARU™

Each cell in an outlined block must contain a digit: a two-cell block contains the digits 1 and 2, a three-cell block contains the digits 1, 2 and 3; and so on. The same digit must not appear in neighbouring cells, not even diagonally.

ARROWORD

An Arroword grid is similar to a Crossword in that conventionally, solutions to clues can be entered in two directions: across, from left to right; and down, from top to bottom. Clues are set in the grid. Arrows indicate where the answers go.

HONEYCOMB

Honeycomb takes its name, naturally enough, from the shape of the grid, a tessellation of hexagons. All the answers are six-letter words. Each answer is entered in a circle around its clue-number. The first letter of the answer is entered in the shaded triangle immediately above the clue number. If the clue number is odd, enter the answer in an anti-clockwise direction. If the clue number is even, enter the answer in a clockwise direction.

JUMBO CODEWORD

Crack the code to fill in the Crossword grid. Each letter of the alphabet makes at least one appearance in the grid and is represented by the same number wherever it appears. A number of letters have been decoded to help with the identification of other letters and words in the grid.

ROUNDABOUT

An elaborate form of continuous Crossword, where answers to clues run in one of four directions: inwards, outwards, clockwise and anti-clockwise. Unusually, one set of answers (outwards) end, rather than begin, on their respective clue numbers.

LOGIC PROBLEM

The object of this puzzle is to use the clues given to link several items together. From the information provided, solvers must deduce who's who, what's what, why, when and how. Where a grid is provided, this is used to record positive and negative relationships. Cross-referencing within the grid may reveal further definite information.

PATHFINDER

Trace a continuous path through all the letters of the grid, starting from the highlighted position and moving one letter at a time, horizontally or vertically, but not diagonally.

JOLLY MIXTURES

Jolly Mixtures takes the form of a Crossword, but each answer is an anagram of the clue. Several words might be formed from the letters of a clue, so part of the challenge is to identify the correct one.

January

Every man should be born again on the first day of January. Start with a fresh page.

Take up one hole more in the buckle if necessary, or let down one, according to circumstances; but on the first day of January let every man gird himself once more, with his face to the front, and take no interest in the things that were and are past.

Henry Ward Beecher

Wordsearch

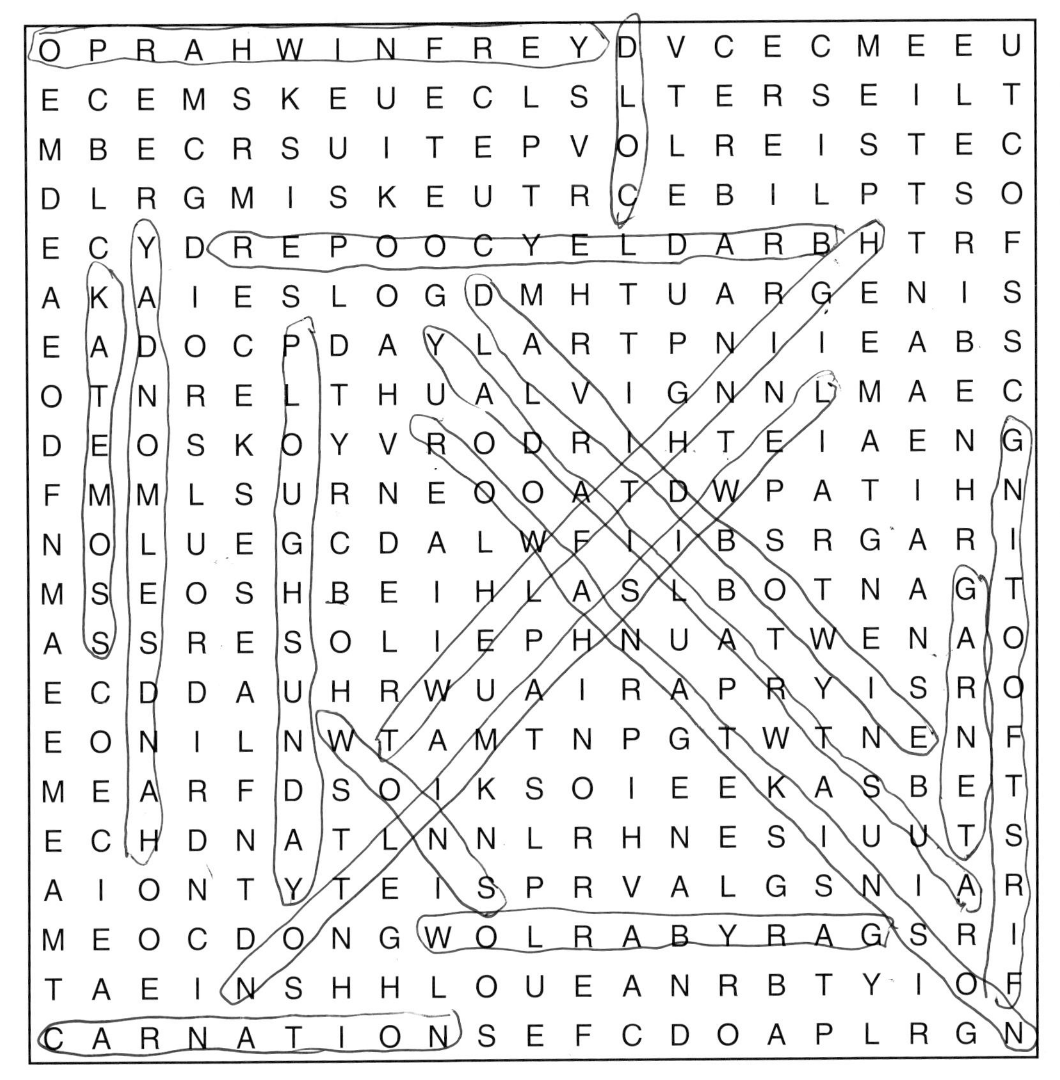

Find all the listed words and phrases associated with January, together with stars celebrating their birthdays this month, hidden in the grid.

AUSTRALIA DAY	FIRST FOOTING	OPRAH WINFREY
BRADLEY COOPER	GARNET	PLOUGH SUNDAY
BURNS NIGHT	GARY BARLOW	ROWAN ATKINSON
CARNATION	HANDSEL MONDAY	SNOW
COLD	KATE MOSS	TWELFTH NIGHT
DAVID BOWIE	LEWIS HAMILTON	
EPIPHANY	NEW YEAR	

THURSDAY *NEW YEAR'S DAY*

1

FRIDAY

2

SATURDAY

3

SUNDAY

4

MONDAY

5

TUESDAY

6

WEDNESDAY

7

THURSDAY

8

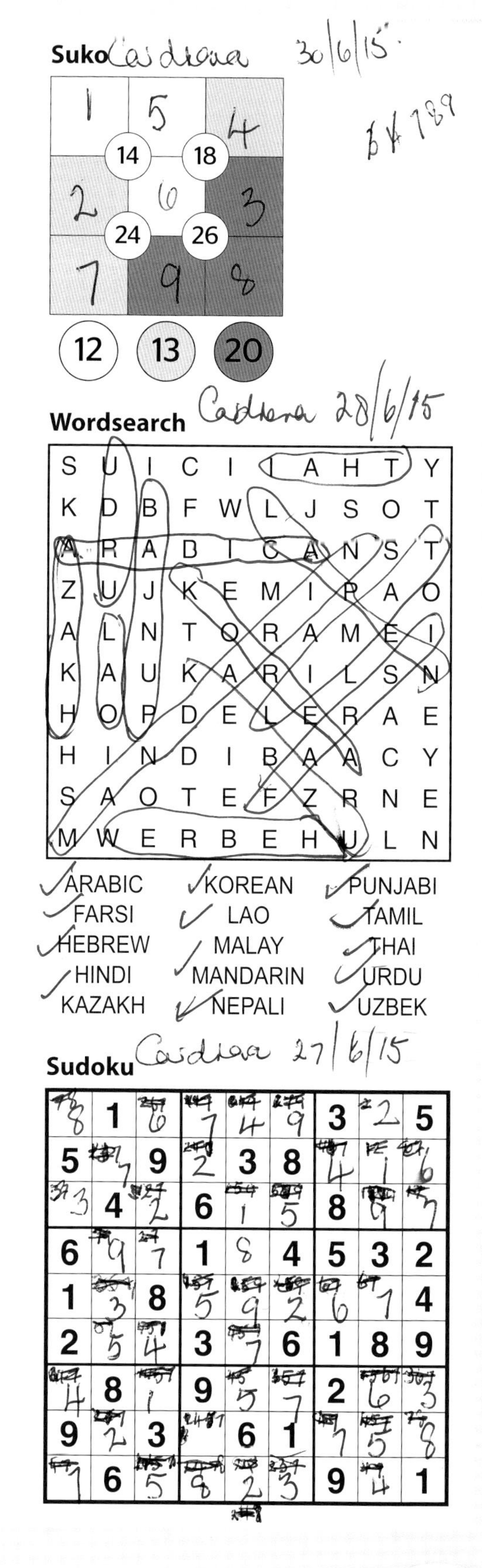

FRIDAY
9

SATURDAY
10

SUNDAY
11

MONDAY
12

TUESDAY
13

WEDNESDAY
14

THURSDAY
15

FRIDAY
16

Number Jig

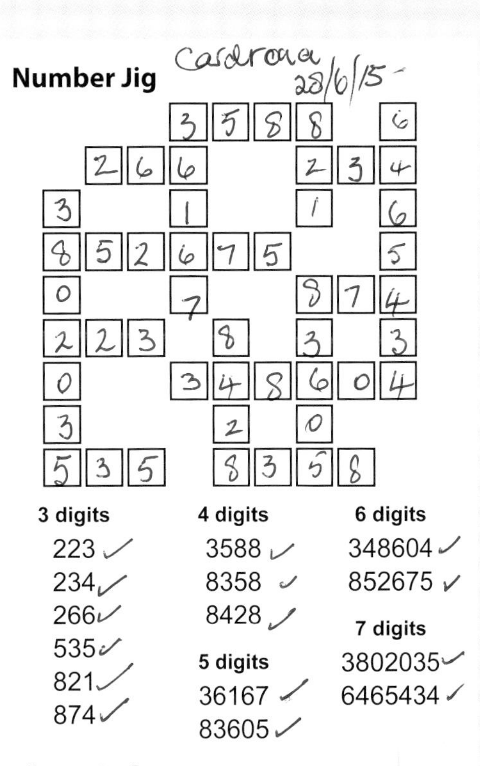

3 digits
223
234
266
535
821
874

4 digits
3588
8358
8428

5 digits
36167
83605

6 digits
348604
852675

7 digits
3802035
6465434

Short Code

A C E L O P R S T W

1 S	2	3	4	5
6	7 T	8	9	10

Dice Maze

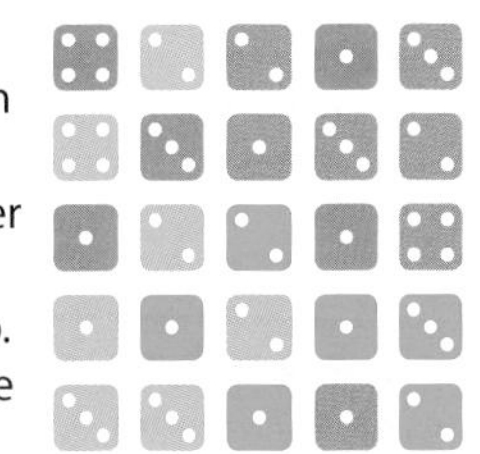

Each colour represents a direction (up, down, left or right) and the number of dots on each dice tell you how far to go. Starting in the middle dice of the maze, follow the directions correctly and you will visit every dice in turn once only. Which dice is the last you visit on your trip?
Purple = Left; Green = Right; Blue = Up; Orange = Down.

SATURDAY
17

SUNDAY
18

MONDAY
19

TUESDAY
20

WEDNESDAY
21

THURSDAY
22

FRIDAY
23

SATURDAY
24

Linkword

GUEST	L	I	S	T	PRICE
FIRM					CREAM
JUMP					OUT
TAG					LEADER
TRAIL					SHEDS
RING					BACK
BICYCLE					GAUGE

Sudoku

Cardrona 18/4/16

Brickwork

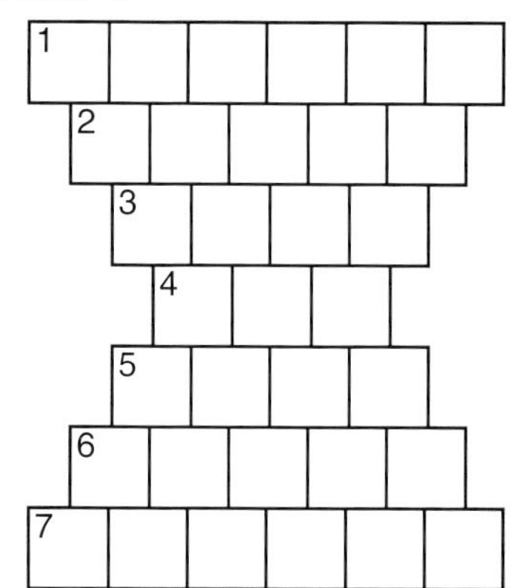

1 Traditional story (6)
2 Narrow shelf (5)
3 Joy, delight (4)
4 Human limb (3)
5 Adhesive (4)
6 Fencing move (5)
7 Dense tropical forest (6)

SUNDAY *BURNS NIGHT*

25

MONDAY

26

TUESDAY

27

WEDNESDAY

28

THURSDAY

29

FRIDAY

30

SATURDAY

31

Add Up

Cardrona 28/6/15

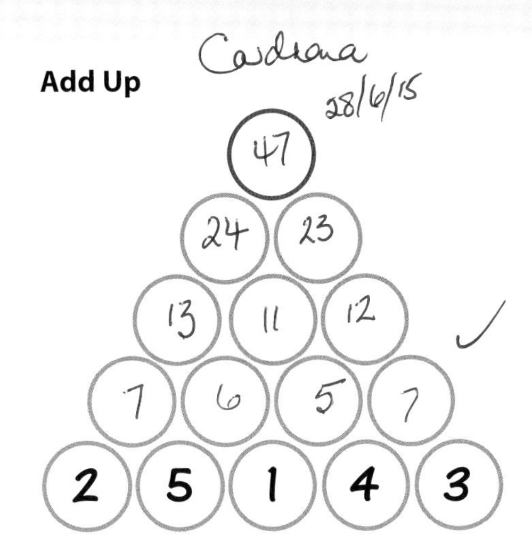

Word Ladder

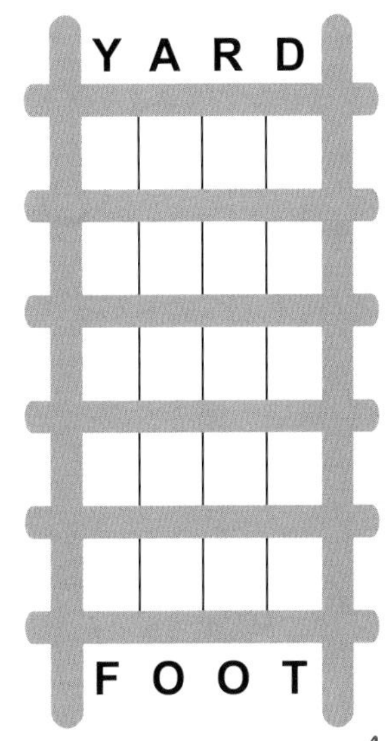

CARDRONA 28/6/15

Suguru

1	2	1	4	1	2	1
3	**4**	2	3	2	4	3
1	5	**1**	4	1	**3**	1
2	3	2	**5**	2	5	2
1	5	**4**	3	4	1	**4**
3	2	1	2	5	3	5
1	4	**3**	4	1	**2**	1

Arroword

- Kids' game (1-3)
- Person who measures land
- Joining together
- Stank
- Give permission for
- Bed, couch
- Mend (socks)
- Humid and muggy
- __ Gibson, actor
- Image of a god
- Broad smile
- Solid water
- Molten volcanic rock
- Pepper grinder
- The Ladies
- Coat of __, family insignia
- One of Alcott's 'Little Women'
- Obtained
- __ -The-Pooh, famous bear
- Tiny amount
- Toy baby
- Woodwind instrument
- Appearance
- __ area, danger zone (2 2)
- Hindu spiritual teacher
- __ stick, child's bouncy toy
- Sticky substance
- Furrow made by wheels
- Filth, usually floating
- Chef
- Female horse
- Large deer
- Central part of a castle
- Inspector, scrutineer
- Golfing stroke
- Travels as a sightseer
- Undo (a skirt or trousers)
- Group of television episodes
- Cloth put under a child's chin
- Sediment
- Nova Scotia's country
- Joint in the leg
- Imprecise
- Turning point, crucial moment
- Uncommon
- Distance from wing tip to wing tip
- Band worn over the shoulder
- __ *Dance*, David Bowie hit
- Hearth-rug
- Sleep late (3,2)
- Male child
- Pleaded
- Catch (a wrongdoer in the act)
- Cathedral dignitary
- Beast of burden or fool
- Dinner jacket
- Garden watering tube
- Shaft of light

The shaded squares will spell out the name of a famous author born in January.

Buried Bones

This dopey dog can't remember where he buried his bones. Can you help him find all ten of them hidden in the picture?

Honeycomb

All the answers are six-letter words. Each answer is entered in a circle around its clue number. The first letter of the answer is entered in the shaded triangle immediately above the clue number. If the clue number is odd, enter the answer in an anti-clockwise direction. If the clue number is even, enter the answer in a clockwise direction.

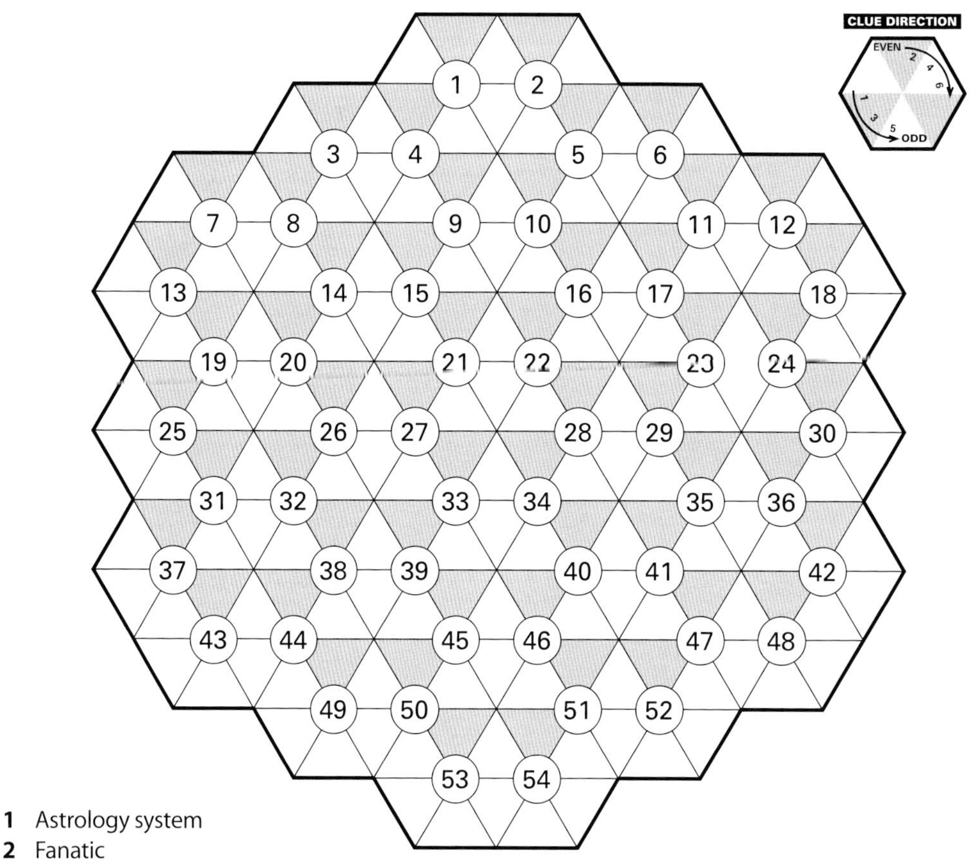

1 Astrology system
2 Fanatic
3 Reduce in rank
4 Make wider
5 B-complex vitamin
6 Stay
7 Inn
8 In current fashion
9 Concealed
10 Mode of speech
11 Crowds
12 Swears
13 Large book
14 Make bare
15 Period of a lease
16 Select
17 Thigh-length trousers
18 Happens again
19 Fine cotton fabric
20 Capital of the Irish Republic
21 In an impolite way
22 In a gentle manner
23 Calamitous
24 Set of instructions
25 High pitched
26 Happen
27 Make ineffective
28 Boned joint
29 In poor condition
30 Dam-building rodent
31 Discarded refuse
32 Room for storing food
33 Most certain
34 Greatest in age
35 In a pleasant manner
36 Wickedly
37 Castle tower
38 Set down in writing
39 Declaim from memory
40 Quantity of medicine
41 Mathematical ratio
42 Introduce gradually
43 Minor mission
44 Large and plump
45 Growing weary
46 Casino activity
47 Sibling's daughters
48 Skin irritations
49 Elephant or wild boar
50 More wealthy
51 Wrongly informed
52 Reflected
53 Ornamental neckband
54 Long thin piece

Two for Tea

ACROSS
1 Come by, acquire (6)
6 Another time (5)
7 Hollow, concave (6)
9 Yawning (5)
12 Hair ornament (5)
14 Indifferent to pleasure or pain (5)
16 Contort (5)
19 Pay out (6)
21 *Mother* ___, panto (5)
22 Pestered, scolded (6)

DOWN
1 Fertile spot (5)
2 Card below the Jack (3)
3 Grandmother, affectionately (4)
4 Spanish sparkling wine (4)
5 Gambling stake (4)
8 Prestige (5)
10 Stood (3,2)
11 Greek letter between upsilon and chi (3)

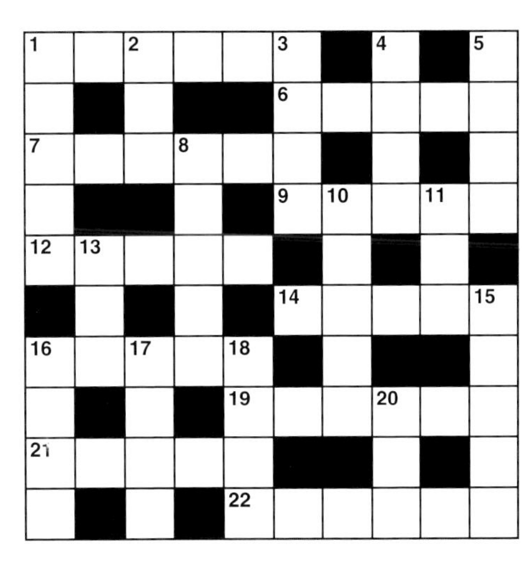

13 Deep sound made by a cow (3)
15 Gave up (power) (5)
16 Roman item of attire (4)
17 Computer symbol (4)
18 Person aged over twelve and under twenty (4)
20 Heart scan (inits)(3)

ACROSS
1 Conductor's stick (5)
4 Dislike intensely (4)
6 French word for 'yes' (3)
7 Main table in a church (5)
8 Informal photograph (4)
9 Granny ___, apple variety (5)
11 Gruff-voiced (5)
13 Hired car and driver (4)
14 Send a message via computer (5)
16 Wicked act (3)
17 Instrument associated with angels (4)
18 South American mountains (5)

DOWN
1 ___ constrictor, snake (3)
2 Tasty morsel (6)
3 Direction of the Arctic Circle (5)
4 Make a noise like a snake (4)
5 Give a job to (6)
9 Grab suddenly (6)
10 Territory surrounded by water (6)
11 'Laughing' wild animal (5)
12 Be unable to pronounce the letter 's' properly (4)
15 ___ Angeles, Hollywood's city (3)

Parrot Fashion

Which of the eight images is the reflection of the parrot?

Pattern Maker

Can you spot the pattern in this sequence, and work out what comes next from the five options?

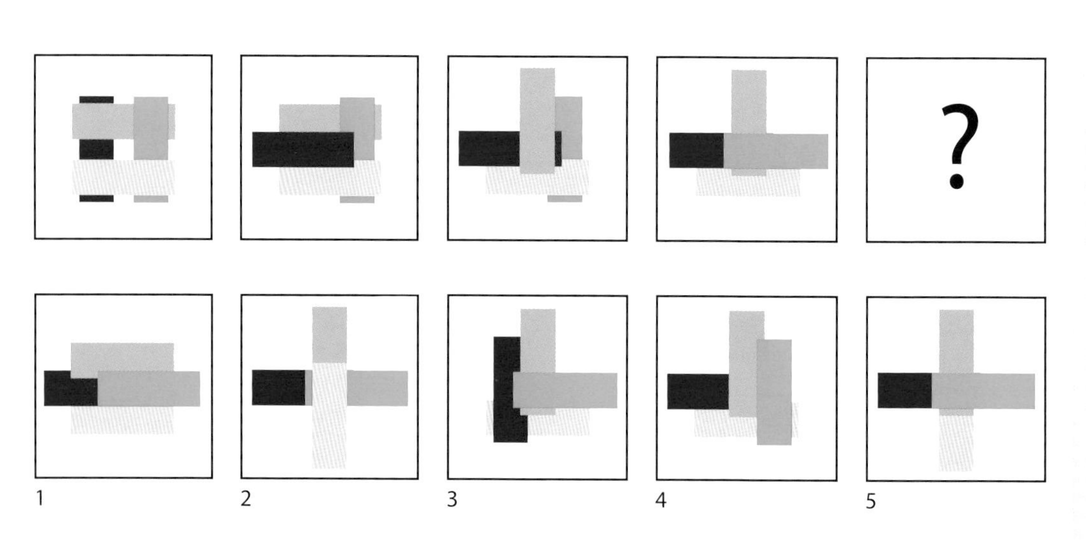

Jumbo Codeword

The letters in the phrase box will spell out an event in January.

22	18	19	18	3	6	12		11	7	8	8	20
3		18			8	23	24	1		16		24
13	23	7		23 I	7 R	14 K		24	18	6		13
7		22	8	3		18	10	8		24	13	26
18	15	16		20		5	8	3		13		26
5		22	18	18	15		7		22	9	13	1
	12		6	7	13	11	18	4	18		17	
14	23	9	23		21		5		2		16	
	6		17	16	13	1		22	6	7	13	1
	12		16		9	18	26		16		7	
19	18	2	18	5		22	24	8	11		23	
	7		6		21		23		24	8	16	5
	6		6	7	8	16	3	21	18		15	
12	8	11	18		21		14	23	6	18		25
13		13		7	8	5		3		24	23	18
10	18	24		8	13	7		21	16	5		6
10		6	9	8		13	22	12		18	13	6
23		7		15	18	3	16			22		18
22	12	1	24	1		14	3	23	6	6	18	5

A B C D E F G H I J K L M N O P Q R S T U V W X Y Z

1	2	3	4	5	6	7	8	9	10	11	12	13
						R						

14	15	16	17	18	19	20	21	22	23	24	25	26
K									I			

18	11	23	11	12	13	3	1
		I					

Roundabout

Solutions to Radial clues (1 to 24) either start from the outer edge of the circle and read inwards, or start from the inner ring and read outwards to the edge (so they are all five-letter words). Solutions to Circular clues read in either a clockwise or an anti-clockwise direction round the circle.

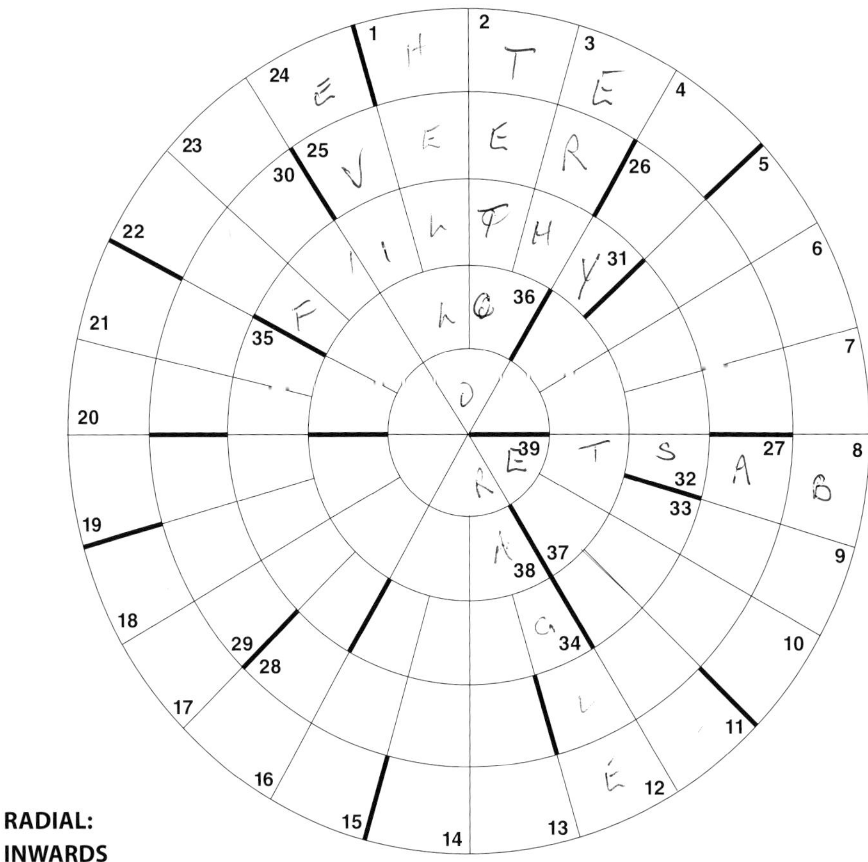

RADIAL:

INWARDS

1 Word of greeting
8 Pour fat over cooking meat
9 Particular condition
10 In that place
12 Edward ___, composer
13 Of the Arctic or Antarctic
14 Direct the course of
15 Michaelmas daisy
16 Rich German tart
17 Wind instrument
19 Make amends
21 Chirp of a small bird
23 Modernise (a ship)

OUTWARDS

2 Group of eight musicians
3 Earthy pigment
4 Perhaps
5 French Impressionist painter
6 Intended, signified
7 Confused fight
11 Rub out
18 Sign up
20 Principle, belief
22 Slightly drunk
24 Oily Mediterranean fruit

CIRCULAR: CLOCKWISE

9 Precipitous
14 Took a seat
17 Result of a puncture (4,4)
26 Under
27 Narrow aperture
28 Piece for a single performer
31 Disgustingly dirty
33 Bird of prey
34 County town of Cornwall

ANTI-CLOCKWISE

5 Projections on a cog wheel
8 Wager
25 Vic ___, comedian and actor
29 Saturated with water
30 Writing implement
32 CS Lewis's lion
35 Aural organ
36 Customer
37 Afternoon meal
38 Distant, far away

Logic Problem

The five swings in the park are all occupied, and each child is being pushed by a female relative. From the following information, can you work out which child is on which swing (numbered left to right from 1 to 5), and the name and relationship of the pusher of each?

Clues

1 Mum is pushing the child on swing 1, who is not Matthew.

2 The aunt is pushing the swing directly between Hannah's and the one being pushed by Grace.

3 Brett is being pushed by Kath, on a swing immediately to the right of the one in the hands of the cousin.

4 Charlotte is being pushed by her sister, whose name does not begin with a J.

5 Swing 3 is being pushed by Joanne.

6 Helen is the grandmother of one of the children.

	Brett	Charlotte	Hannah	Matthew	Sarah	Grace	Helen	Jenny	Joanne	Kath	Aunt	Cousin	Grandmother	Mother	Sister
1															
2															
3															
4															
5															
Aunt															
Cousin															
Grandmother															
Mother															
Sister															
Grace															
Helen															
Jenny															
Joanne															
Kath															

Swing	Child	Pusher	Relationship

Pathfinder

Beginning with the letter M in the shaded square, follow a single path to find 18 words connected to winter sports. The trail passes through every letter once and may twist up, down and sideways (but never diagonally).

ALPINE	NORDIC
BIATHLON	RACE
BOBSLEIGH	SKATING
CURLING	SKELETON
FREESTYLE	SKIING
ICE HOCKEY	SLALOM
JUMP	SLEDGE
LUGE	SNOWBOARD
MOUNTAIN	SPEED

M	I	A	T	H	L	O	N	L	U	G
O	B	D	R	O	L	A	L	S	G	E
U	N	O	A	M	K	A	T	I	N	S
A	T	B	N	S	S	C	O	C	I	L
I	N	W	O	O	N	K	H	E	E	E
O	B	E	D	T	E	E	Y	R	G	D
B	S	E	N	O	L	E	K	A	C	E
E	L	P	S	R	E	S	S	G	N	J
I	Y	L	E	D	N	K	I	I	I	U
G	T	S	E	I	I	P	G	N	L	M
H	F	R	E	C	A	L	C	U	R	P

Solutions

Wordsearch

O	P	R	A	H	W	I	N	F	R	E	Y	D	V	C	E	C	M	E	E	U
E	C	E	M	S	K	E	U	E	C	L	S	L	T	E	R	S	E	I	L	T
M	B	E	C	R	S	U	I	T	E	P	V	O	L	R	E	I	S	T	E	C
D	L	R	G	M	I	S	K	E	U	T	R	C	E	B	I	L	P	T	S	O
E	C	Y	D	R	E	P	O	O	C	Y	E	L	D	A	R	B	H	T	R	F
A	K	A	I	E	S	L	O	G	D	M	H	T	U	A	R	G	E	N	I	S
E	A	D	O	C	P	D	A	Y	L	A	R	T	P	N	I	I	E	A	B	S
O	T	N	R	E	L	T	H	U	A	L	V	I	G	N	N	L	M	A	E	C
D	E	O	S	K	O	Y	V	R	O	D	R	I	H	T	E	I	A	E	N	G
F	M	M	L	S	U	R	N	E	O	O	A	T	D	W	P	A	T	I	H	N
N	O	L	U	E	G	C	D	A	L	W	F	I	I	B	S	R	G	A	R	I
M	S	E	O	S	H	B	E	I	H	L	A	S	L	B	O	T	N	A	G	T
A	S	S	R	E	S	O	L	I	E	P	H	N	U	A	T	W	E	N	A	O
E	C	D	D	A	U	H	R	W	U	A	I	R	A	P	R	Y	I	S	R	O
E	O	N	I	L	N	W	T	A	M	T	N	P	G	T	W	T	N	E	N	F
M	E	A	R	F	D	S	O	I	K	S	O	I	E	E	K	A	S	B	E	T
E	C	H	D	N	A	T	L	N	N	L	R	H	N	E	S	I	U	U	T	S
A	I	O	N	T	Y	T	E	I	S	P	R	V	A	L	G	S	N	I	A	R
M	E	O	C	D	O	N	G	W	O	L	R	A	B	Y	R	A	G	S	R	I
T	A	E	I	N	S	H	H	L	O	U	E	A	N	R	B	T	Y	I	O	F
C	A	R	N	A	T	I	O	N	S	E	F	C	D	O	A	P	L	R	G	N

Sudoku

8	1	6	7	4	9	3	2	5
5	7	9	2	3	8	4	1	6
3	4	2	6	1	5	8	9	7
6	9	7	1	8	4	5	3	2
1	3	8	5	9	2	6	7	4
2	5	4	3	7	6	1	8	9
4	8	1	9	5	7	2	6	3
9	2	3	4	6	1	7	5	8
7	6	5	8	2	3	9	4	1

Linkword

LIST, HAND, BAIL, TEAM, BIKE, PULL, TYRE **THIMBLE**

Sudoku

1	6	8	3	4	9	5	2	7
2	4	5	1	6	7	9	8	3
9	7	3	2	8	5	4	1	6
8	5	9	6	1	4	7	3	2
6	3	4	7	2	8	1	9	5
7	2	1	9	5	3	6	4	8
5	9	2	4	3	6	8	7	1
3	8	7	5	9	1	2	6	4
4	1	6	8	7	2	3	5	9

Number Jig

			3	5	8	8		6
	2	6	6			2	3	4
3			1			1		6
8	5	2	6	7	5			5
0			7			8	7	4
2	2	3		8		3		3
0			3	4	8	6	0	4
3				2		0		
5	3	5		8	3	5	8	

Suko

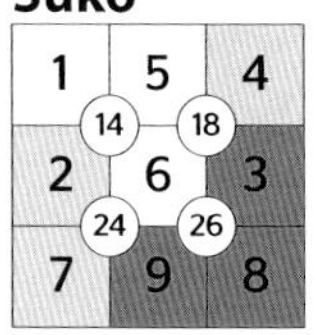

Short Code

S	E	C	R	A
O	T	P	L	W

Brickwork

LEGEND
LEDGE
GLEE
LEG
GLUE
LUNGE
JUNGLE

Add Up

47

Word Ladder

YARD, lard, lord, word, wood, food, FOOT

Wordsearch

S	U	I	C	I	I	A	H	T	Y
K	D	B	F	W	L	J	S	O	T
A	R	A	B	I	C	A	N	S	T
Z	U	J	K	E	M	I	P	A	O
A	L	N	T	O	R	A	M	E	I
K	A	U	K	A	R	I	L	S	N
H	O	P	D	E	L	E	R	A	E
H	I	N	D	I	B	A	A	C	Y
S	A	O	T	E	F	Z	R	N	E
M	W	E	R	B	E	H	U	L	N

Dice Maze

The final dice in your trip is the blue 1, fourth dice in the fourth row.

Suguru

1	3	1	4	1	3	1
2	4	2	3	2	4	2
1	5	1	4	1	3	1
2	3	2	5	2	5	2
1	5	4	3	4	1	4
3	2	1	2	5	3	5
1	4	3	4	1	2	1

Solutions

Arroword

A.A. Milne

Kids' Corner

Honeycomb

1 Zodiac 2 Maniac 3 Demote 4 Dilate 5 Niacin 6 Remain 7 Tavern 8 Modern 9 Latent 10 Accent 11 Masses 12 Curses 13 Volume 14 Denude 15 Tenure 16 Choose 17 Shorts 18 Recurs 19 Muslin 20 Dublin 21 Rudely 22 Softly 23 Tragic 24 Rubric 25 Shrill 26 Befall 27 Defuse 28 Fillet 29 Ailing 30 Beaver 31 Litter 32 Larder 33 Surest 34 Eldest 35 Nicely 36 Evilly 37 Turret 38 Record 39 Recite 40 Dosage 41 Cosine 42 Instil 43 Errand 44 Rotund 45 Tiring 46 Gaming 47 Nieces 48 Itches 49 Tusker 50 Richer 51 Misled 52 Echoed 53 Choker 54 Sliver.

Two for Tea

Parrot Fashion

8

Pattern Maker

Panel 2. With each progression, the furthest back shape turns through 90 degrees and moves to the front.

Jumbo Codeword

Epiphany

Roundabout

RADIAL: 1 Hello 2 Octet 3 Ochre 4 Maybe 5 Manet 6 Meant 7 Mêlée 8 Baste 9 State 10 There 11 Erase 12 Elgar 13 Polar 14 Steer 15 Aster 16 Torte 17 Flute 18 Enrol 19 Atone 20 Tenet 21 Tweet 22 Tipsy 23 Refit 24 Olive.

CIRCULAR: 5 Teeth 8 Bet 9 Steep 14 Sat 17 Flat tyre 25 Reeves 26 Beneath 27 Slot 28 Solo 29 Wet 30 Pen 31 Filthy 32 Aslan 33 Eagle 34 Truro 35 Ear 36 Client 37 Tea 38 Remote.

Logic Problem

Kath is pushing Brett, but not on swing 1 (clue 3) and Helen is the grandmother (clue 6), so the sister who is pushing Charlotte and who is neither Joanne nor Jenny (clue 4), must be Grace. Joanne is pushing swing 3 (clue 5), so Hannah is not being pushed by her mother on swing 1 (clues 1 and 2). Mum is also not pushing Matthew (clue 1), so her child must be Sarah. We know that her Mum is not Joanne, Grace, Helen or Kath, so she must be Jenny. Brett is not being pushed by his cousin (clue 3) or grandmother (clue 6), so it must be his aunt, leaving the cousin as Joanne, pushing swing 3. From clue 2, the aunt must be pushing swing 4, so Hannah must be on swing 3 and Grace must be the sister pushing swing 5 (clues 2 and 4). Therefore Hannah must be being pushed by her cousin and, by elimination, Helen must be pushing her grandson Matthew, who must be on swing 2.

In summary: 1, Sarah, Jenny, mother. 2, Matthew, Helen, grandmother. 3, Hannah, Joanne, cousin. 4, Brett, Kath, aunt. 5, Charlotte, Grace, sister.

Pathfinder

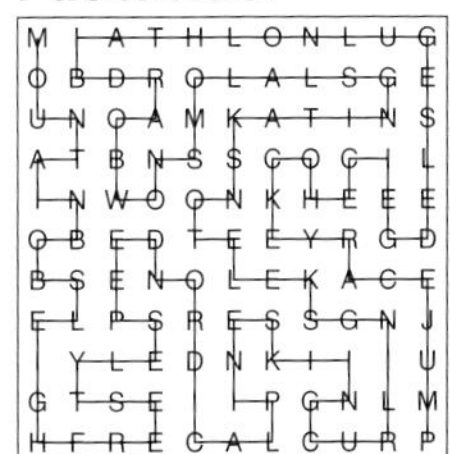

February

2015 – The Chinese Year of the Sheep

The most creative sign in the Chinese zodiac, those born in the Year of the Sheep (also known as the Year of the Ram or Goat) are often artistic, sensitive, sweet and charming. Outwardly dreamy and starry-eyed, Sheep are inwardly anxious, insecure, and usually find day-to-day living difficult and puzzling.

Sheep are not overly ambitious, but once they find work that makes use of their considerable talents, they are passionate about what they do. Typically surrounded by beautiful things, Sheep have an ardent love of creature comforts and are almost always elegantly dressed, but can become overly reliant on appearances. Conversely, Sheep people have an innate love of nature and are never happier than when messing about in the garden.

Wordsearch

Find all the listed words associated with Chinese New Year.

CHINESE
CLEAN
DECORATIONS
DRAGONS
DUMPLINGS
FAMILY
FIREWORKS
FORTUNE
FRIENDS
GIFTS
HAPPINESS
LION DANCE
LONGEVITY
LUNAR
MANDARINS
MEAL
MONEY
NEW YEAR
NIAN GAO
RED ENVELOPES
RELATIVES
RICE
SPRING FESTIVAL
TRADITION
VISITING
WEALTH
ZODIAC

SUNDAY
1

MONDAY
2

TUESDAY
3

WEDNESDAY
4

THURSDAY
5

FRIDAY
6

SATURDAY
7

SUNDAY
8

Suko

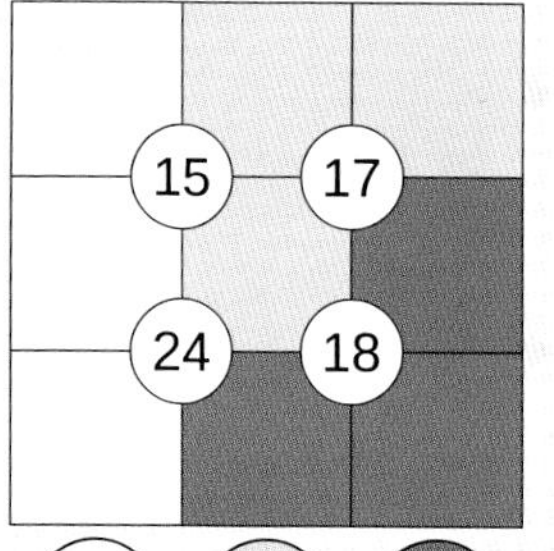

14 16 15

Wordsearch

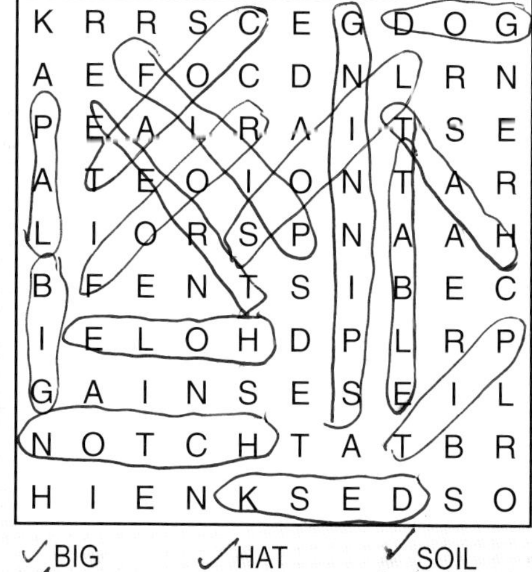

BIG
COAT
DESK
DOG
FLIP
HAT
HOLE
LAP
NOTCH
ROOF
SOIL
SPINNING
TABLE
TIP
TREE

Sudoku

	9	3					1	
2		1	3				5	
4	5		8	1		2		
	6	2		5			7	8
		9	7		6			
				2		5	9	
		5			8			4
8	7		2		5		3	
			4			9		

MONDAY
9

TUESDAY
10

WEDNESDAY
11

THURSDAY
12

FRIDAY
13

SATURDAY *VALENTINE'S DAY*
14

SUNDAY
15

MONDAY
16

Number Jig

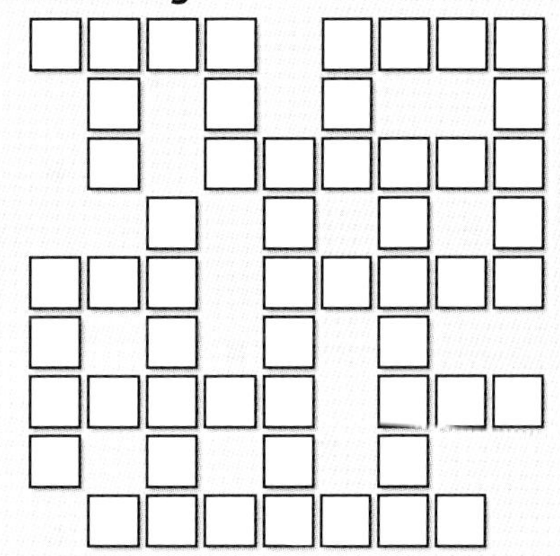

3 digits
288
565
607
936
969

4 digits
1569
2552
6038

5 digits
25746
33243
58386

6 digits
628977
770220

7 digits
2755325
5075414
9633921

Short Code

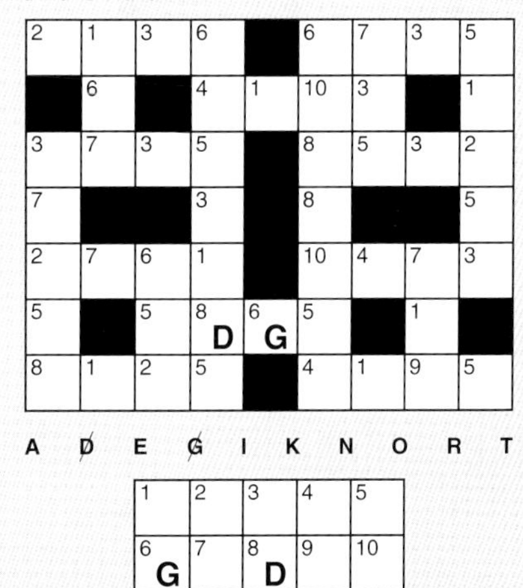

Sum People

Each of the characters in this sum box represents a different number, with the added total of the numbers at the end of each row and column. Work out the value of each character and fill in the question mark.

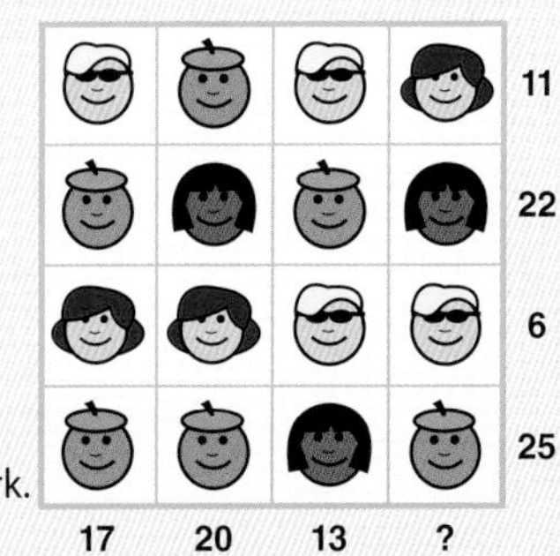

TUESDAY *SHROVE TUESDAY*

17

WEDNESDAY *ASH WEDNESDAY*

18

THURSDAY

19

FRIDAY

20

SATURDAY

21

SUNDAY

22

MONDAY

23

TUESDAY

24

Linkword

HORROR					SET
CALENDAR					DOT
CASH					JOB
BUS					PRESS
REED					DOWN
ACID					GOAL
STAND					CHAIR

Sudoku

4			8				7	
	8		5	9	2			
9	7					1		
						2		
6	1		2			7	5	
3								
7			9		3	8		
2	5	9	6		7		4	

Brickwork

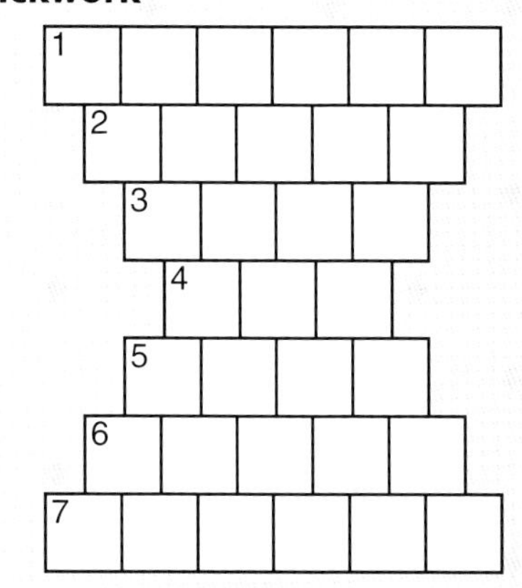

1 Made of timber (6)
2 Possessed (5)
3 Clive _, actor (4)
4 Odd number (3)
5 *Finding _*, animated film (4)
6 Evil spirit, fiend (5)
7 Up-to-date (6)

WEDNESDAY
25

THURSDAY
26

FRIDAY
27

SATURDAY
28

NOTES

Add Up

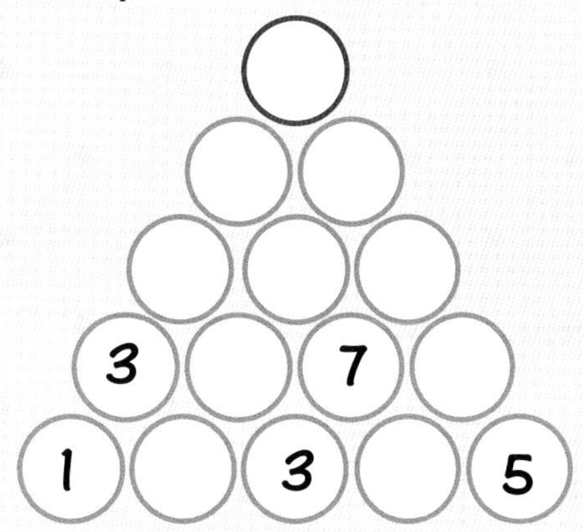

Word Ladder

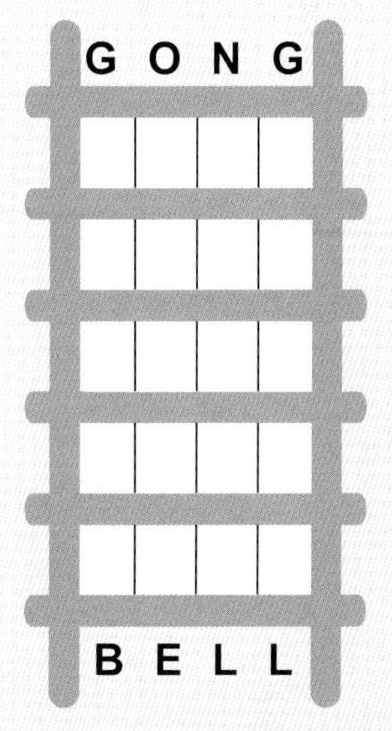

Suguru

	1		2			
						2
	3				5	3
	4					
3		5		1		3

Crossword

The shaded squares will spell out the name of a festival which occurs during this month.

ACROSS
1 Toboggan (4)
6 Continuous dull pain (4)
8 Pantomime story with a genie (7)
9 Crime of violence (inits)(3)
11 Metal can (3)
13 Coating on stale food (5)
16 Game also called housey-housey (5)
18 Bacterium that can cause food poisoning (1,4)
19 Brother's daughter (5)
20 David ___ George, early 20th-century Liberal PM (5)
21 Cost of an item (5)
22 ___ on, encourage (4)
25 River dam (4)
27 Charge for using a bridge (4)
28 Unit of electricity (4)
29 The two together (4)
31 Tax paid on imports (4)
34 Put off, hinder (5)
37 Uncontrolled rush (5)
38 Release from bonds (5)
39 Ordinary dress, not uniform (5)
40 Egypt's capital (5)
43 Nude, unclothed (5)
46 Resort with mineral spring attraction (3)
49 Ask for money (3)
50 ___ whispers, party game (7)
51 Unlit (4)
52 Job to be performed (4)

DOWN
2 Company trademark (4)
3 Roald ___, *Charlie and the Chocolate Factory* author (4)
4 Adult male (3)
5 Groom's response (1,2)
6 Opposed to (4)
7 Attach to a hook on the wall (4)
10 Desk or office (6)
12 Money received from your work (6)
13 Take away sign (5)
14 Profound (4)
15 ___ Bear, Boo Boo's cartoon pal (4)
16 Bitter digestion fluid (4)
17 Greater in age (5)
23 Snap taken by a camera (5)
24 Actor brother of Joseph Fiennes (pictured) (5)
25 Greeted with a hand signal (5)
26 Small cove or bay (5)
29 Fundamental (5)
30 Root vegetable (6)
32 Quick on the ___, swift to understand (6)
33 Give way or surrender (5)
34 Protest march (4)
35 Bland soya-based foodstuff with a silky texture (4)
36 Destroy (4)
41 India's continent (4)
42 Toast holder (4)
44 Aid (a criminal) (4)
45 White and yellow food items (4)
47 Put a match to (3)
48 Only a handful (3)

Jigword

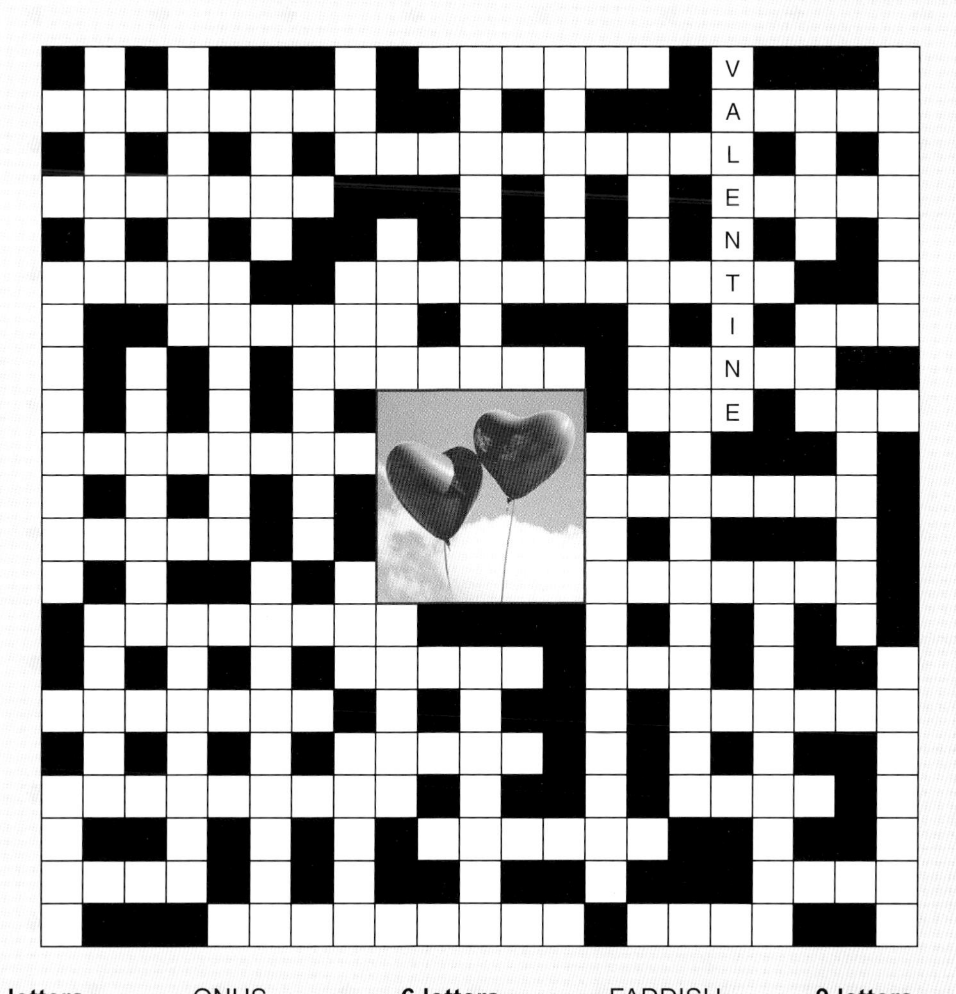

3 letters
BED
DIE
HEM
LOG
MIL
RAT
SHE
SIR

4 letters
DATE
EURO
HALO
LOVE
MISS
ONUS
ROSE
SODA

5 letters
ADORE
ARRAY
CLOVE
DRIED
ENNUI
EXUDE
FLUID
UNITY
WAGON
WREST

6 letters
ANTHEM
ATOMIC
LAUREL
OFFCUT
RECOIL
RIBBON
STATUE
TUNNEL

7 letters
CHICANE
DESPAIR
DESTROY
ECSTASY
EVOKING
FADDISH
FAINTED
FLOWERS
IMPLORE
INHABIT
PROPOSE
REVERIE
TORPEDO

8 letters
CAREFREE
CHICKPEA
FANCIFUL
INDIRECT
TENTACLE

9 letters
AERODROME
MEETING UP
SECONDARY
SKEDADDLE
~~VALENTINE~~

10 letters
MEANINGFUL

11 letters
CIRCULATION
MASCULINITY
NIGHTINGALE

Logic Sequence

The blocks below have been rearranged in the same pattern but in different positions. Can you work out the new arrangement from the clues below?

The blue shapes are now one on top of the other.
The vowels are both on the bottom row.
The red shapes are both on the right hand side.
The b is bordered by the m and g only.

Two Timer

Two sets of clues to the same answers.

CRYPTIC CLUES

ACROSS

1 Material wealth only? (8)
7 Commander elected another time (5)
8 Is it elegant having one braid twisted? (8)
10 Raise from afar when rocket is launched (4-3)
11 Given a good press? (6)
13 Demand some more questions (7)
16 Shot towards the green bit of potato (4)
18 Some nutritious items are included in it (4)
19 A bar etc arranged for show (7)
22 Jack takes Scotsman to runway (6)
23 We called and left during argument (7)
25 Tania included clown stopping short in the country (8)
26 Do better as forty of the Romans do – pronouncedly (5)
27 His pony's suffering mesmerism (8)

DOWN

1 Worn portion of fish? (8)
2 From bus coins thrown but not at a great speed! (8)
3 Rang me about early Christian resting-place (6)
4 Bird run over by train (4)
5 Number one vice? (7)
6 Second judge uncertain (5)
9 Rugby quartet included permitted stream (7)
12 Damage of flat due to be put right (7)
14 Station for a time in America (8)
15 Win convincingly although not in form! (8)
17 Playwright Harold pens article for artist (7)
20 Strong man consuming some nectar zanily (6)
21 Round before ten, snoop round to find someone voting for another (5)
24 Effortless entering the asylum (4)

STRAIGHT CLUES

ACROSS

1 Fabric woven from fine goats' hair (8)
7 Moreover, besides (5)
8 Charming, confident (8)
10 Flight's commencement (4-3)
11 Smoothed out the creases (6)
13 Entreaty (7)
16 Piece of silicon in computers (4)
18 List of food choices (4)
19 Nightclub entertainment (7)
22 Road-surfacing material (6)
23 Dispute noisily (7)
25 Country south of Kenya (8)
26 Outshine (5)
27 Trance inducement (8)

DOWN

1 Pouch attached to a man's breeches in the past (8)
2 Below the sound barrier (8)
3 Trough or box in a stable (6)
4 Hand support on stairs (4)
5 Extreme self-interest (7)
6 Trice, instant (5)
9 Small brook (7)
12 Failure to pay one's debts (7)
14 End of a transport route (8)
15 Surpass in quality (8)
17 Interior decorator (7)
20 Man raised by an ape in the jungle (6)
21 Agent for an absent person (5)
24 Simple to do (4)

Quiz Wordsearch

Answer the given clues and then find the answers hidden in the grid.

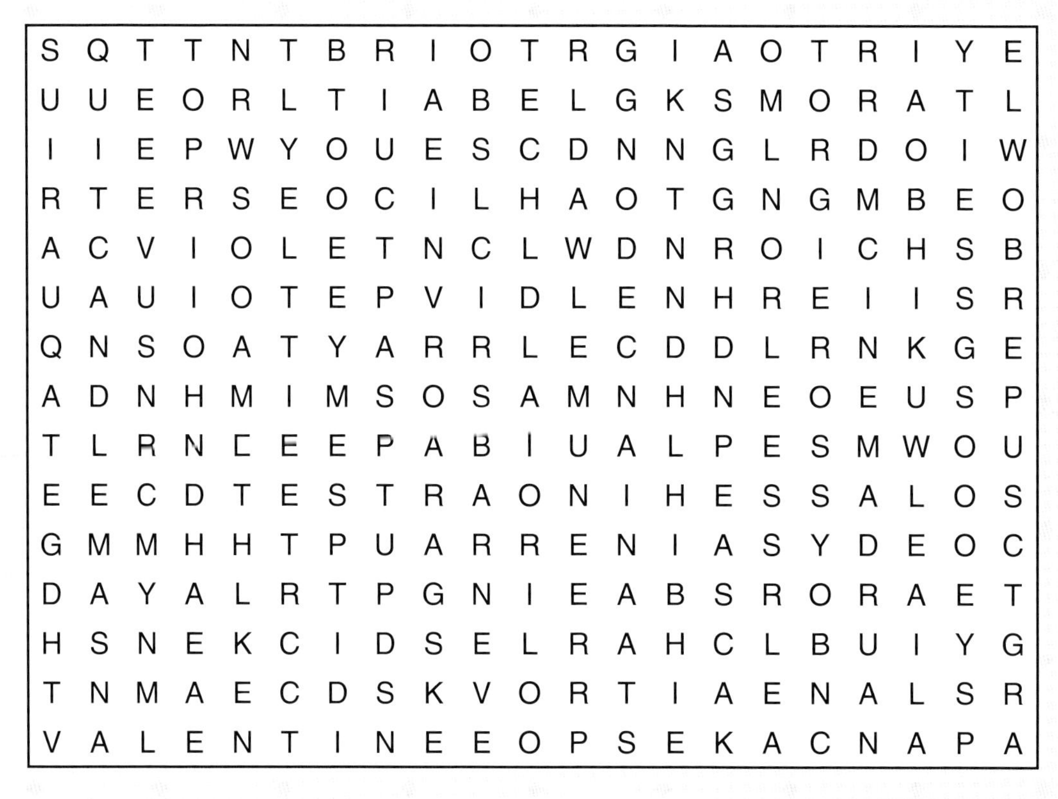

1 16th US president born 12th February 1809 (7,7)

2 19th-century English author born 7th February 1870 (7,7)

3 American football championship game played on the first Sunday in February (5,4)

4 Birth sign of someone born in early February (8)

5 Early spring flowers (9)

6 February 2 in the US (9,3)

7 Festival of the purification of the Virgin Mary (9)

8 Love token sent in February (9)

9 Movie theatre, the first in Britain opened 20th February 1896 (6)

10 Purple birthstone for February (8)

11 Shrove Tuesday food (8)

12 Small purple flower, birth flower for February (6)

13 South Asian country which celebrates its Independence Day on the 4th (3,5)

14 Start of Lent in the Western Christian calendar (3,9)

15 Winter sport (6)

16 Woolly ruminant, symbol of the coming Chinese Year (5)

Logic Problem

Five young women each have names identical to those of literary heroines of the past, but each is following a very contemporary career in a different part of the country. From the clues given below, can you match the five young women with their occupations, homes and ages?

Clues

1 Emma Woodhouse is two years older than the policewoman.

2 The young woman based in Bolton is called Becky Sharp; she is older than Jane Eyre.

3 The resident of Weston-super-Mare is a year older than the young woman from Croydon.

4 The nursery teacher lives and works in Colchester.

5 The journalist is a year younger than Elizabeth Bennett.

6 The young woman aged 25 operates the telephone switchboard of a busy company.

7 Mary Barton is 26 years old.

	Journalist	Model	Nursery teacher	Policewoman	Switchboard operator	Bolton	Colchester	Croydon	Swindon	Weston-super-Mare	23	24	25	26	27
Becky Sharp															
Elizabeth Bennett															
Emma Woodhouse															
Jane Eyre															
Mary Barton															
23															
24															
25															
26															
27															
Bolton															
Colchester															
Croydon															
Swindon															
Weston-super-Mare															

Name	Occupation	Location	Age

Jolly Mixtures

ACROSS
1 THE SAINT
6 FIST
8 SAMS
9 PREMISED
10 EDDA
11 A LITRE
13 NEVE
15 PARES
17 GATES
19 BAHT
21 BATHER
24 DYED
26 COUNTERS
27 ARTY
28 MANE
29 ATTENDER

DOWN
2 A SEER
3 DINE, SIR
4 AMUSES
5 MERIT
6 STEEL
7 FLEEING
12 EATS
14 VETS
16 PREFORM
18 THEREAT
20 BLEATS
22 ROANS
23 HORNE
25 PADRE

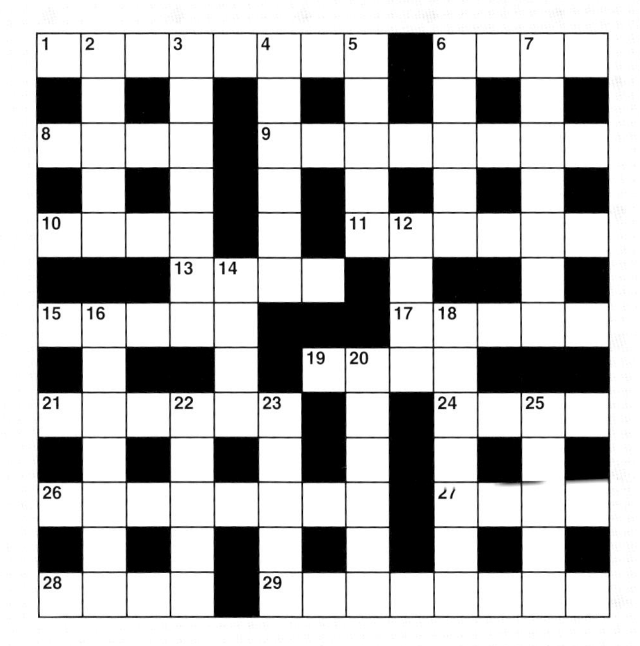

Solutions

Wordsearch

K Z H U H U S E V I T A L E R K T H U C T
O V I S I T I N G N L T M A C R H U O S T
P E A L R E L O I A T Y E C L R M S A D K
H N E O L U O A T R E A L P S W O E C N D
T U R A U E N R E D E N V E L O P E S E S
L T O G N G G M H T U A R E S S Y E S I O
C R D A A L E R T P E A S P O R E K T R H
U O L O R I V G M A L E R E C D R S R F K
O F S S E N I P P A H I R T S O I I A E N
D R L S R E T T E O N S P A W E C W T I H
E N A Y U E Y M R G C D N E Z E N L S R G
C D A E M O E I F A T N R I A O R I E S O
O L R I Y T N E E S D I C F R D D A H E H
R R U A P W S S N G F I A E O A I I C C L
A A T G G T E A N N M M T E R F D N A S K
T O I Y I O E N A I I E C I D N A N T C L
I R H V E L N S U L Y A I O O D N T A E P
O R A W C A L S Y P G E S I N N M E O M C
N L D N S T F I G M R T N O A W E A L T H
S E I S H L O U E U A N I O R T Y I S E F
C D O A P L R G N D M L T E M I S A K H E

Number Jig

1	5	6	9		2	5	5	2
	6		3		8			5
	5		6	2	8	9	7	7
		7		7		6		4
6	0	7		5	8	3	8	6
0		0		5		3		
3	3	2	4	3		9	6	9
8		2		2		2		
	5	0	7	5	4	1	4	

Linkword

FILM, YEAR, DESK, STOP, PIPE, DROP, EASY **MYSTERY**

Sudoku

5	2	6	3	7	4	9	1	8
4	9	3	8	6	1	5	7	2
1	8	7	5	9	2	4	3	6
9	7	2	4	5	6	1	8	3
8	3	5	7	1	9	2	6	4
6	1	4	2	3	8	7	5	9
3	4	8	1	2	5	6	9	7
7	6	1	9	4	3	8	2	5
2	5	9	6	8	7	3	4	1

Short Code

T	A	N	G	■	G	O	N	E
■	G	■	R	A	I	N	■	A
N	O	N	E	■	D	E	N	T
O	■	■	N	■	D	■	■	E
T	O	G	A	■	I	R	O	N
E	■	E	D	G	E	■	A	■
D	A	T	E	■	R	A	K	E

A	T	N	R	E
G	O	D	K	I

Suko

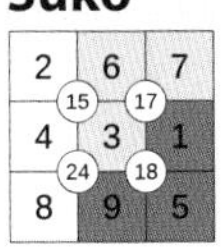

Wordsearch

K R R S C E G D O G
A E F O C D N L R N
P E A L R A I T S E
A T E O I O N T A R
L I O R S P N A A H
B F E N T S I B E C
I E L O H D P L R P
G A I N S E S E I L
N O T C H T A T B R
H I E N K S E D S O

Brickwork

WOODEN
OWNED
OWEN
ONE
NEMO
DEMON
MODERN

Add Up

48

Sudoku

6	9	3	5	4	2	8	1	7
2	8	1	3	6	7	4	5	9
4	5	7	8	1	9	2	6	3
1	6	2	9	5	4	3	7	8
5	3	9	7	8	6	1	4	2
7	4	8	1	2	3	5	9	6
9	1	5	6	3	8	7	2	4
8	7	4	2	9	5	6	3	1
3	2	6	4	7	1	9	8	5

Sum People

14

Word Ladder

GONG, gone, gene, gent, bent, belt, BELL

Suguru

3	1	3	2	3	5	4
2	5	4	5	4	1	2
4	3	1	3	2	5	3
5	2	5	4	1	4	1
1	4	1	2	3	2	5
3	2	5	4	1	4	3
4	1	3	2	5	2	1

Solutions

Crossword

Candlemas

Quiz Wordsearch

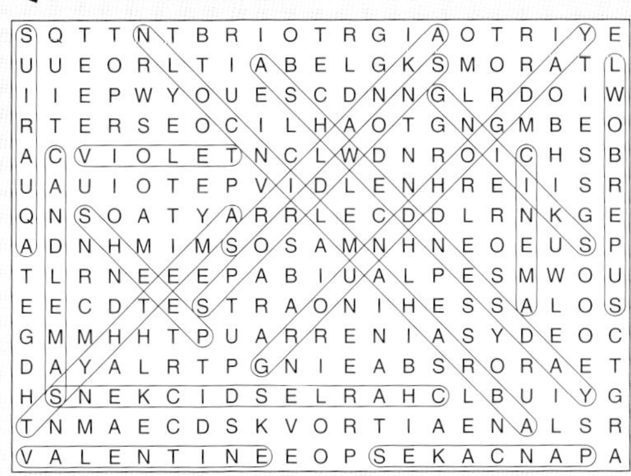

1 ABRAHAM LINCOLN
2 CHARLES DICKENS
3 SUPERBOWL
4 AQUARIUS
5 SNOWDROPS
6 GROUNDHOG DAY
7 CANDLEMAS
8 VALENTINE
9 CINEMA
10 AMETHYST
11 PANCAKES
12 VIOLET
13 SRI LANKA
14 ASH WEDNESDAY
15 SKIING
16 SHEEP

Jigword

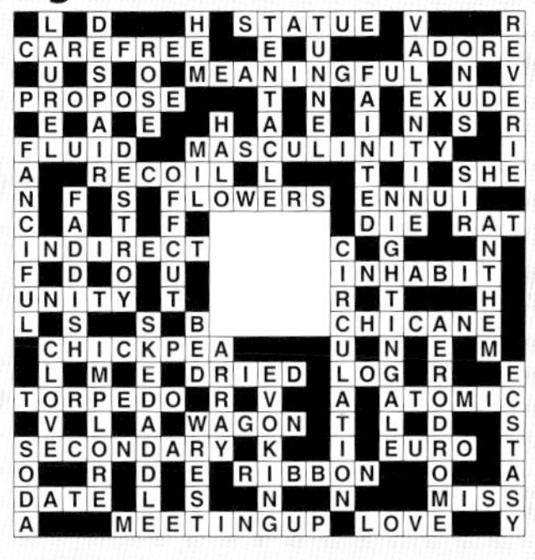

Logic Sequence

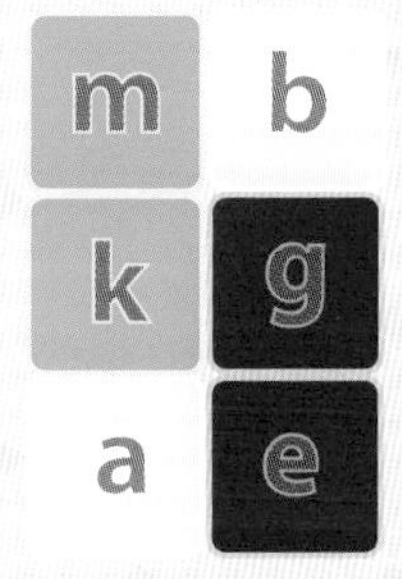

Two Timer

ACROSS: 1 Cashmere 7 Again 8 Debonair 10 Lift-off 11 Ironed 13 Request 16 Chip 18 Menu 19 Cabaret 22 Tarmac 23 Wrangle 25 Tanzania 26 Excel 27 Hypnosis.
DOWN: 1 Codpiece 2 Subsonic 3 Manger 4 Rail 5 Egotism 6 Jiffy 9 Rivulet 12 Default 14 Terminus 15 Outclass 17 Painter 20 Tarzan 21 Proxy 24 Easy.

Logic Problem

The policewoman cannot be 26 or 27 (clue 1), and the woman aged 25 is a switchboard operator (clue 6). Since Mary Barton is 26 (clue 7), clue 1 rules out 24 as the policewoman's age, so she must be 23, and Emma Woodhouse must be the switchboard operator aged 25. So the policewoman cannot be Becky Sharp, from Bolton (clue 2), or Elizabeth Bennett (clue 5), and her age rules out Mary Barton, so she must be Jane Eyre. Clue 5 also tells us Elizabeth Bennett cannot be 24, so, by elimination, she must be 27, leaving Becky Sharp's age as 24. So, from clue 5, Mary Barton, aged 26, must be the journalist. We have now matched four names with occupations or locations, so the nursery teacher who lives in Colchester (clue 4) must be Elizabeth Bennett, which leaves Becky Sharp as the model. From clue 3, the young woman from Weston-super-Mare must be journalist Mary Barton, aged 26, and the one from Croydon must be Emma Woodhouse, aged 25, which leaves Jane Eyre as a policewoman based in Swindon.
In summary: Becky Sharp, model, Bolton, 24. Elizabeth Bennett, nursery teacher, Colchester, 27. Emma Woodhouse, switchboard operator, Croydon, 25. Jane Eyre, policewoman, Swindon, 23. Mary Barton, journalist, Weston-super-Mare, 26.

If March comes in like a lion, it'll go out like a lamb.
If it comes in like a lamb, it'll go out like a lion.

British weather lore proverb about March winds

Wordsearch

X	B	V	J	B	U	U	Y	E	L	T	H	G	I	N	K	A	R	I	E	K
T	I	B	D	T	P	N	S	U	E	T	E	N	S	R	E	G	L	T	G	M
B	N	R	E	A	N	S	U	E	I	T	E	P	O	V	L	I	N	R	E	I
S	O	O	P	T	F	Y	E	L	C	R	G	G	N	M	I	A	R	I	E	S
S	S	E	O	D	U	F	T	R	N	S	E	E	B	I	L	R	P	S	W	O
E	R	T	R	F	N	N	O	I	E	R	I	A	S	L	O	C	G	C	M	H
T	E	U	A	R	C	A	E	D	G	N	Q	P	I	Y	S	L	E	L	O	C
A	H	L	R	T	P	O	R	C	I	U	N	I	S	N	E	E	A	O	B	S
O	P	R	E	T	H	U	M	G	A	L	L	T	H	I	G	I	N	C	M	A
E	C	C	S	K	V	N	O	M	N	R	P	O	T	I	A	N	E	K	N	F
S	A	L	S	R	A	E	A	O	O	A	J	E	P	A	W	A	T	S	I	H
T	M	N	Y	W	U	R	E	C	T	N	I	D	R	L	S	D	R	F	G	A
D	E	M	E	O	I	B	E	R	O	I	W	L	T	A	N	A	R	O	E	S
A	L	O	L	N	I	T	I	T	N	E	C	E	A	D	H	A	H	R	R	U
V	L	P	E	S	E	C	L	O	I	L	A	T	A	R	G	H	N	W	M	E
I	E	R	F	S	K	E	K	O	I	Y	A	B	E	L	T	C	C	A	D	N
D	T	L	R	S	H	E	S	U	A	I	O	N	T	E	T	S	P	R	R	W
S	V	X	D	A	E	N	O	T	S	D	O	O	L	B	L	H	U	D	A	G
D	S	A	T	H	E	I	D	E	S	O	F	M	A	R	C	H	D	A	I	M
A	Y	M	E	O	C	D	N	R	T	A	E	I	S	H	L	O	U	A	E	A
Y	N	R	B	T	Y	I	S	E	F	C	E	Q	U	I	N	O	X	D	Y	O

Find all the listed words and phrases associated with March, together with stars celebrating their birthdays this month, hidden in the grid.

AQUAMARINE
ARIES
AUSTRALIAN GRAND PRIX
BLOODSTONE
CLOCKS FORWARD
COMMONWEALTH DAY
DAFFODIL
DANIEL CRAIG
ELLE MACPHERSON
ELTON JOHN
EQUINOX
EWAN MCGREGOR
KEIRA KNIGHTLEY
MARCH HARE
PISCES
ST DAVID'S DAY
ST PATRICK'S DAY
THE IDES OF MARCH

SUNDAY ST DAVID'S DAY

1

MONDAY

2

TUESDAY

3

WEDNESDAY

4

THURSDAY

5

FRIDAY

6

SATURDAY

7

SUNDAY

8

Suko

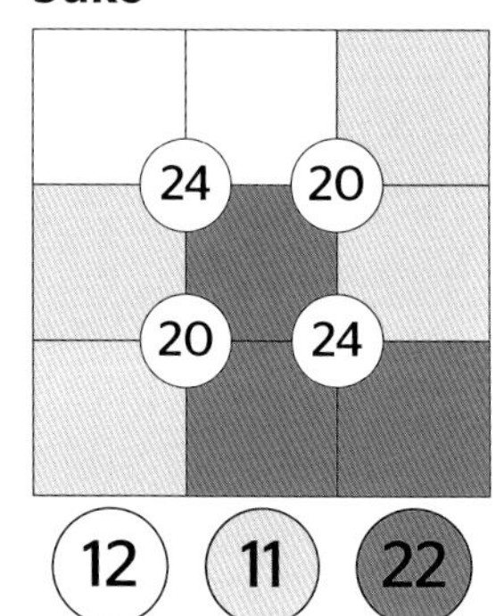

Wordsearch

E	V	I	T	I	S	O	P	O	D
Y	F	W	N	E	D	W	U	L	N
N	S	H	T	M	G	T	A	M	P
E	C	A	H	I	A	R	R	T	A
U	I	O	N	G	U	Y	U	L	T
T	T	L	E	O	G	C	I	S	L
R	A	N	M	R	D	V	R	S	O
A	T	O	E	P	E	E	C	I	V
L	S	N	E	A	R	T	H	D	C
R	E	E	S	U	F	A	I	N	S

AMP
ANODE
CIRCUIT
EARTH
ENERGY
FUSE
LIVE
NEUTRAL
OHM
OUTAGE
POSITIVE
STATIC
SURGE
VOLT
WATT

Sudoku

		5	7			9	2	
				8	4			5
	2		9		6			1
	7		8			4	3	
	9	2	1				8	
	4			6	2	7		9
		3		7				4
			5	1	9	2		
6								

MONDAY *COMMONWEALTH DAY*
9

TUESDAY
10

WEDNESDAY
11

THURSDAY
12

FRIDAY
13

SATURDAY
14

SUNDAY *MOTHER'S DAY*
15

MONDAY
16

Number Jig

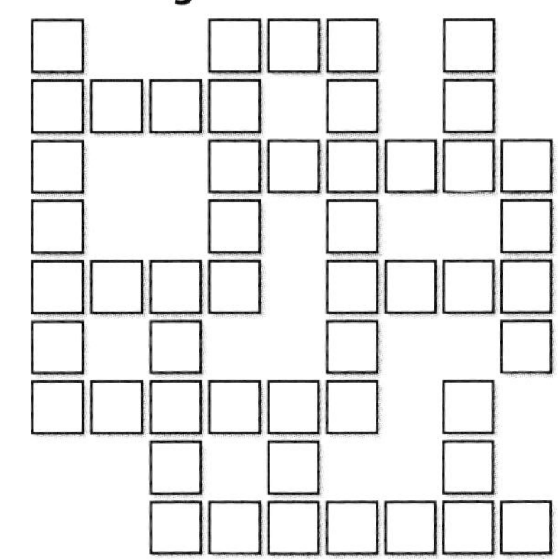

3 digits	4 digits	6 digits
220	4024	721047
462	4118	942304
475	4122	
872	4772	

5 digits
22163
88922

7 digits
2520427
3825657
9402467

Short Code

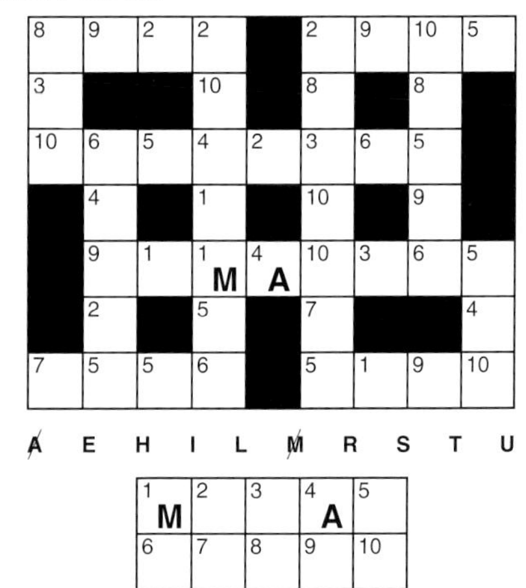

Traffic Lights

Complete the grid so that each row and column contains a red, yellow and green light. The lights at the end of each column and row tell you the colour of the first light you will meet as you move up or down the column, or side to side across the row.

TUESDAY 17 ST PATRICK'S DAY

WEDNESDAY 18

THURSDAY 19

FRIDAY 20

SATURDAY 21

SUNDAY 22

MONDAY 23

TUESDAY 24

Linkword

STUFF					RACE
PACK					RASH
HOME					SHARK
SEA					CUB
SET					BOARD
GENOA					STAND
DEAD					TIME

Sudoku

				4	8	9		
					2	3		
						5	8	
				7	4		9	
5			8	1	9			
8	7		5	6			4	
3	4	7						
		2	1		7		5	3
							2	

Brickwork

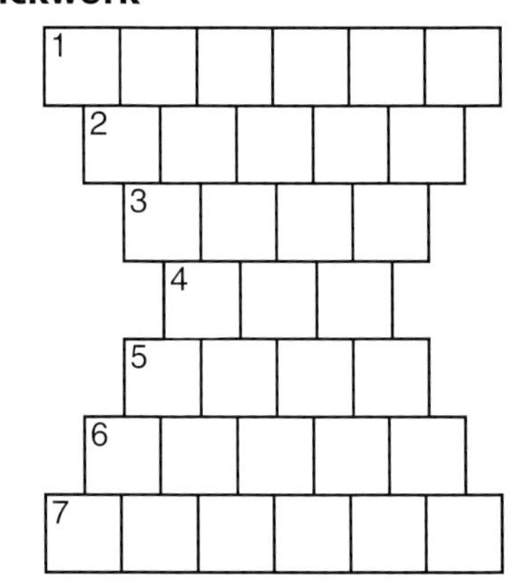

1 Absolute truth (6)

2 Slant, tilt (5)

3 Flatfish (4)

4 ___ Angeles, US city (3)

5 Coin opening (4)

6 Took by theft (5)

7 Lodging place (6)

WEDNESDAY
25

THURSDAY
26

FRIDAY
27

SATURDAY
28

SUNDAY *BRITISH SUMMERTIME BEGINS*
29

MONDAY
30

TUESDAY
31

Add Up

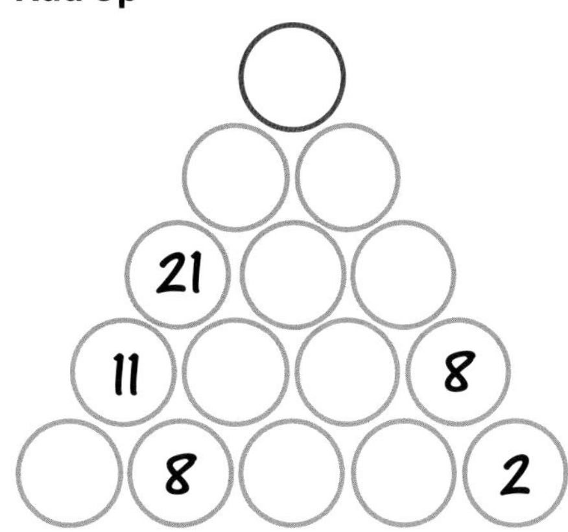

Word Ladder

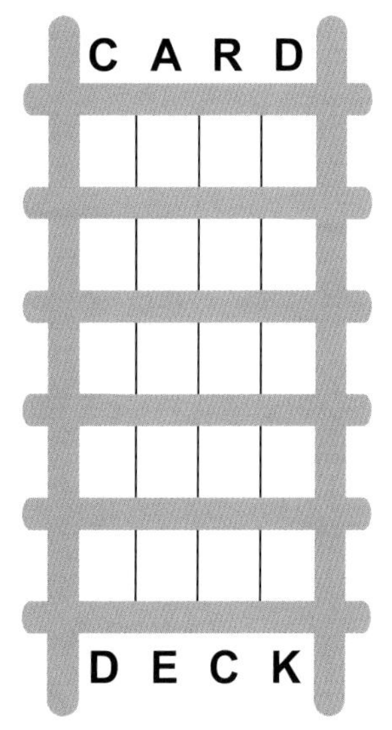

Suguru

4	2			5		
	1			1		
3			4			
			1			1
5						
			2			

Arroword

Grows old
Polite and generous
Burnt remains
Adult or child, person
Clothing tag
UK nobleman
Log material
Liv ___, US actress

First name of actress Ms Thurman
Absent

Mad March animal (pictured)
Cured pig meat
Ballpoint pen
Intense enthusiasm

High or low playing-card
Trickle or leak slowly out

Ignorant lout
___ Diego, US city
Someone you borrow from

Shade of blue
Seventh month of the year
Second-hand
Shout loudly, bawl

Play music in the street
Type, kind

Inform
Not as great in amount

Chinese sauce

Security system (inits)
Loop, spiral
Dame ___ Lynn, singer
Benicio ___ Toro, actor

Thomas Hardy heroine
Fiscal, monetary
(Had) spotted

Star sign
Fawn colour

Expensive wool
Bench in a church
Syrupy topping
Long yellow fruit

Tilt
Pierced body part (3,4)

Circus tent (3,3)
Towards (the wind)
Large brass instrument
Bad smell
Cameron ___, US film star
Affectionate name for grandma

Matt ___, Hollywood star
Fish – common with chips

Hyper-sensitive, obsessive
Waterproof coat

Couch
Make illegal
White rabbit with pink eyes

Look long and steadily
Rotter, bounder

Rearrange the shaded letters to spell out an event in March.

Dot-to-dot

Connect the dots to see a new arrival on the farm.

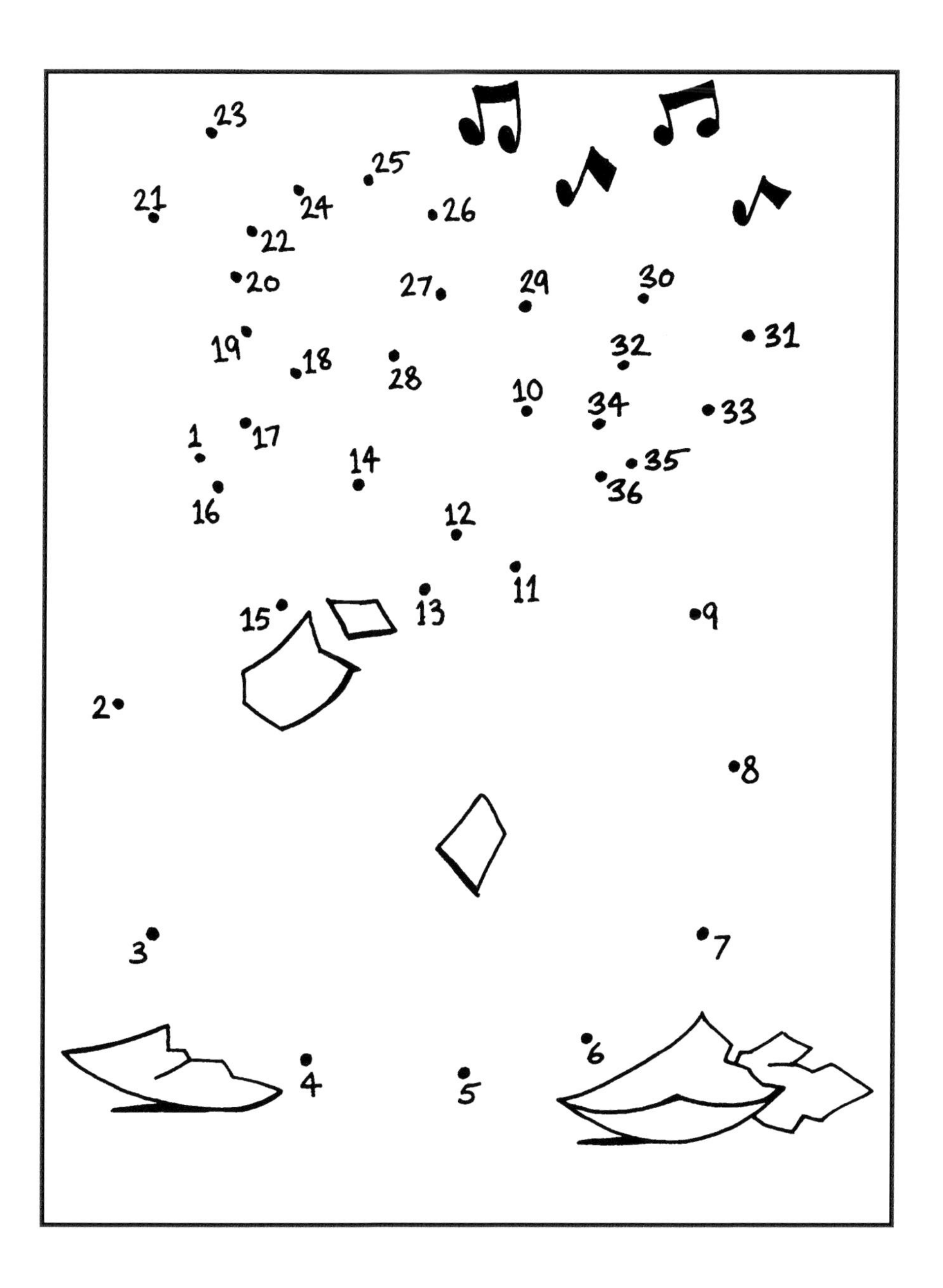

Honeycomb

All the answers are six-letter words. Each answer is entered in a circle around its clue number. The first letter of the answer is entered in the shaded triangle immediately above the clue number. If the clue number is odd, enter the answer in an anti-clockwise direction. If the clue number is even, enter the answer in a clockwise direction.

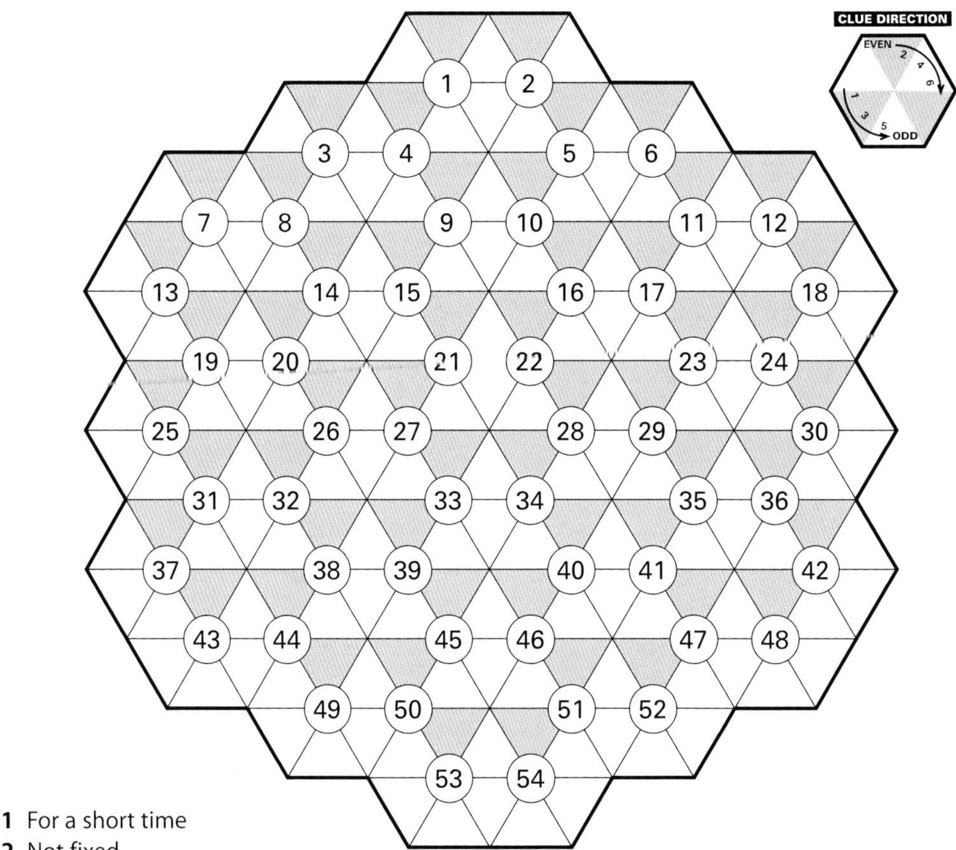

1 For a short time
2 Not fixed
3 Neater
4 Further up
5 Shellfish soup
6 Collect
7 Buy back
8 Jewelled tiara
9 Phantoms
10 Crouches
11 Baby's bed
12 Large fortified building
13 Resolve
14 Agreement
15 Happens
16 Central Italian region
17 Sauntered
18 Eject liquid
19 Be indecisive
20 Duty schedule
21 Went quickly
22 Pressed clothes
23 In high spirits
24 Took a chance
25 Despite the fact that
26 Fracture support
27 Spatter
28 Call into question
29 Small computer application
30 Loud cry of a bird
31 Culpable of a crime
32 Subtle distinction
33 Specimen
34 Bubbling sound
35 Young eels
36 Falters
37 Block up (a hole)
38 Golfer's aide
39 Wildly impulsive
40 Running quickly
41 Cease to occupy
42 Journey
43 Finding enjoyable
44 Not working
45 Clear from a charge
46 Foolish person
47 Submitted for discussion
48 Obtained
49 Distinctive uniform
50 Prey
51 Idiots
52 Electronic noises
53 Esoteric
54 Stoat's fur

Two for Tea

ACROSS

1 Fundamental principle (5)
4 Held (4)
6 20cwt (3)
7 ___ Arabia, desert kingdom (5)
8 Was under an obligation to repay (4)
9 Symbol or theme (5)
11 Steed (5)
13 Greek liqueur (4)
14 Uncooked Italian sauce (5)
16 Female rabbit (3)
17 Wander, travel (4)
18 Evade craftily (5)

DOWN

1 Public vehicle (3)
2 Filthy (6)
3 Difficult to bend (5)
4 Tie securely (4)
5 Walk like a small child (6)
9 Autobiographical account (6)
10 Levered (apart) (6)
11 Felt optimistic (5)
12 Protuberance (4)
15 Poem (3)

ACROSS

1 Fairies' cave (6)
6 Continuous humming sound (5)
7 Muddled, confused (6)
9 Discard as useless (5)
12 Loose covering for the shoulders (5)
14 Tidy and clean feathers with the beak (5)
16 Frock (5)
19 Foreign-looking, glamorous (6)
21 Person held as property (5)
22 Take the ___, commit yourself (6)

DOWN

1 Mirror material (5)
2 Antique (3)
3 Likelihood, as in gambling (4)
4 Lacking money (4)
5 Shed tears (4)
8 CS ___, creator of Narnia (5)
10 Monte ___, Mediterranean city (5)
11 Gorilla, eg (3)
13 Belonging to that woman (3)
15 Small recess in a wall (5)
16 Table for writing on (4)
17 Academic test (4)
18 Ooze, trickle (4)
20 Darkening of the skin in sunlight (3)

Battleships

The numbers on the side and bottom of the grid indicate occupied squares or groups of consecutive occupied squares in each row or column. Can you finish the grid so that it contains three Cruisers, three Launches and three Buoys so that the numbers tally?

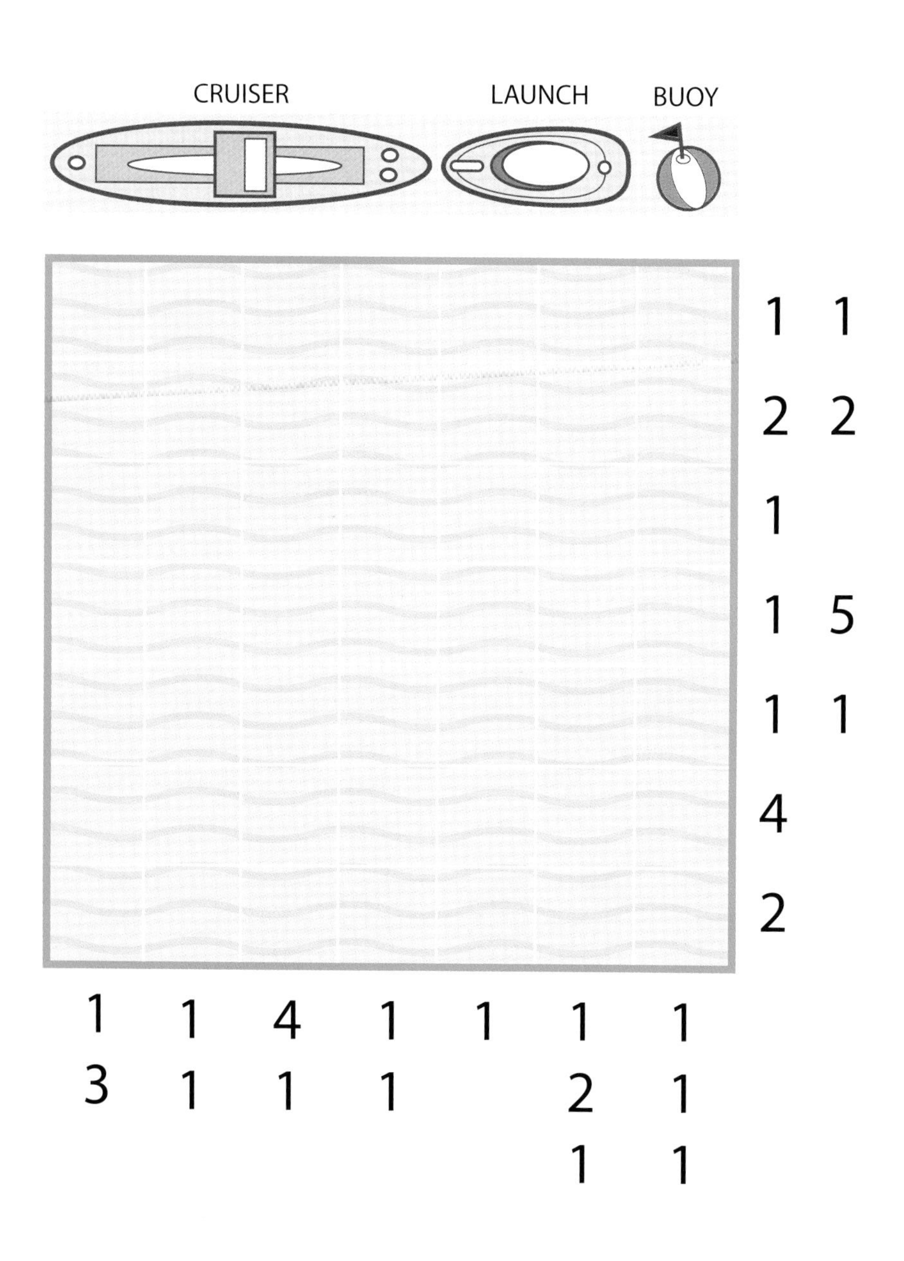

Jumbo Codeword

The letters in the phrase box will spell out the name of a landmark which opened in 1889.

23	9	9	23	9	25	15	■	5	7	5	19	12
9	■	4	■	■	24	12	4	1	■	14	■	4
18	5	22	■	15 S	16 P	2 Y	■	21	23	12	■	1
17	■	22	23	16	■	17	5	5	■	5	21	21
8	15	5	■	4	■	5	9	22	■	9	■	4
14	■	22	4	4	1	■	7	■	23	22	17	2
■	1	■	8	9	23	19	4	26	9	■	23	■
16	4	8	12	■	9	■	2	■	12	■	16	■
■	15	■	15	17	23	1	■	20	5	26	15	5
■	3	■	4	■	1	8	1	■	26	■	12	■
13	8	1	8	15	■	22	8	1	16	■	23	■
■	23	■	26	■	12	■	26	■	26	24	19	2
■	12	■	19	17	23	1	24	12	5	■	11	■
19	4	1	5	■	24	■	17	24	12	5	■	18
8	■	8	■	24	26	19	■	15	■	24	25	4
18	5	6	■	16	24	26	■	12	24	26	■	26
18	■	6	23	16	■	23	19	2	■	9	8	21
5	■	17	■	24	26	5	24	■	■	5	■	23
22	10	5	17	17	■	22	26	5	24	22	5	22

A B C D E F G H I J K L M N O ~~P~~ Q R ~~S~~ T U V W X ~~Y~~ Z

1	2	3	4	5	6	7	8	9	10	11	12	13
	Y											
14	**15**	**16**	**17**	**18**	**19**	**20**	**21**	**22**	**23**	**24**	**25**	**26**
	S	P										

5	23	18	18	5	17		12	4	10	5	26

Roundabout

Solutions to Radial clues (1 to 24) either start from the outer edge of the circle and read inwards, or start from the inner ring and read outwards to the edge (so they are all five-letter words). Solutions to Circular clues read in either a clockwise or an anti-clockwise direction round the circle.

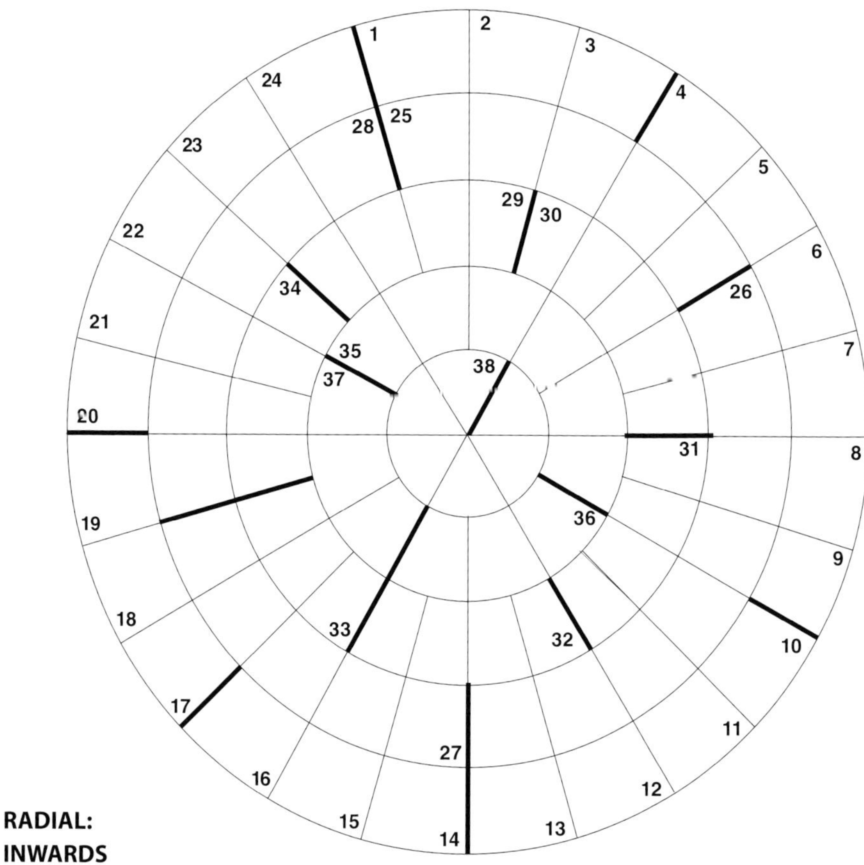

RADIAL:

INWARDS

1 Send-up, hoax
6 Useful or valuable thing
7 Piece of paper
9 Digging tool
11 Thread, filament
12 Being broadcast (2,3)
14 Performer
15 Chief monk
16 To do with the Sun
17 Use bad language
18 Viper
21 Passage between seats
22 Look fixedly

OUTWARDS

2 Aesop's moral story
3 Side of a gem
4 Give medical attention to
5 Buying and selling
8 Film star Mr Murphy
10 Blow up (volcano)
13 Finger ornaments
19 Bridle-straps
20 ___ John, pop star
23 Rigidly upright
24 Sudden raid

CIRCULAR:

CLOCKWISE

1 Coagulate, become firm
4 Provokes playfully
20 Unpleasant
25 Make an emotional appeal
26 Transporting by sea
27 Large group of people
30 Come to an end
31 Paint carelessly
32 Prefix meaning 'against'
33 Went in front
35 Made a sound like a lion
36 2016 Olympic city

ANTI-CLOCKWISE

13 Of a drink, non-alcoholic
16 Health resort
19 Elite regiment (inits)
28 Film director's cry
29 Tedious person
34 Italian sparkling wine
37 Meadow
38 Domesticated polecat

Logic Problem

The first five people to visit a small branch library one afternoon each returned a book, and took out one of a different type. From the clues given below, can you place the women in the order in which they arrived at the library, and describe the book each returned, and the one each borrowed?

Clues

1 The biography was returned by the woman who entered the library immediately before the one who took out a classic which had recently been featured on television.

2 Diana was the fourth woman to put in an appearance.

3 The returned classic was exchanged for a romance, but not by Jean, who was not the third person to arrive.

4 Kelly took out a mystery yarn, which was not the type of book the first visitor brought back.

5 The travel book was brought in by Josephine, who was the next to arrive after Marianne.

6 The second library user borrowed the biography.

7 The book returned by the fifth patron of the afternoon was a romance.

						Books returned					Books borrowed				
	First	Second	Third	Fourth	Fifth	Biography	Classic	Mystery	Romance	Travel	Biography	Classic	Mystery	Romance	Travel
Diana															
Jean															
Josephine															
Kelly															
Marianne															
Books borrowed: Biography															
Classic															
Mystery															
Romance															
Travel															
Books returned: Biography															
Classic															
Mystery															
Romance															
Travel															

Name	Order	Returned	Borrowed

Pathfinder

Beginning with the letter S in the shaded square, follow a single path to find 16 Commonwealth countries. The trail passes through every letter once and may twist up, down and sideways (but never diagonally).

AUSTRALIA	NEW ZEALAND
BOTSWANA	NIGERIA
CANADA	SINGAPORE
FIJI	SOUTH AFRICA
KENYA	SRI LANKA
MALAWI	SWAZILAND
MALTA	THE BAHAMAS
MAURITIUS	TONGA

N	A	A	T	L	Y	N	M	A	I	S
K	L	S	M	A	A	E	A	E	R	O
A	I	R	A	O	T	K	L	G	T	U
T	N	G	G	N	I	A	A	I	H	A
H	I	A	P	A	L	I	W	N	R	F
E	S	I	O	R	T	A	N	D	I	C
B	I	J	R	E	S	U	A	R	U	A
A	F	A	W	S	Z	I	L	I	A	C
H	A	N	S	W	A	U	I	T	M	A
A	M	O	T	A	L	S	N	E	A	N
S	A	B	D	N	A	E	Z	W	D	A

Solutions

Wordsearch

X	B	V	J	B	U	U	Y	E	L	T	H	G	I	N	K	A	R	I	E	K
T	I	B	D	T	P	N	S	U	E	T	E	N	S	R	E	G	L	T	G	M
B	N	R	E	A	N	S	U	E	I	T	E	P	O	V	L	I	N	R	E	I
S	O	O	P	T	F	Y	E	L	C	R	G	G	N	M	I	A	R	I	E	S
S	S	E	O	D	U	F	T	R	N	S	E	E	B	I	L	R	P	S	W	O
E	R	T	R	F	N	N	O	I	E	R	I	A	S	L	O	C	G	C	M	H
T	E	U	A	R	C	A	E	D	G	N	Q	P	I	Y	S	L	E	L	O	C
A	H	L	R	T	P	O	R	C	I	U	N	I	S	N	E	E	A	O	B	S
O	P	R	E	T	H	U	M	G	A	L	L	T	H	I	G	I	N	C	M	A
E	C	C	S	K	V	N	O	M	N	R	P	O	T	I	A	N	E	K	N	F
S	A	L	S	R	A	E	A	O	O	A	J	E	P	A	W	A	T	S	I	H
T	M	N	Y	W	U	R	E	C	T	N	I	D	R	L	S	D	R	F	G	A
D	E	M	E	O	I	B	E	R	O	I	W	L	T	A	N	A	R	O	E	S
A	L	O	L	N	I	T	I	T	N	E	C	E	A	D	H	A	H	R	R	U
V	L	P	E	S	E	C	L	O	I	L	A	T	A	R	G	H	N	W	M	E
I	E	R	F	S	K	E	K	O	I	Y	A	B	E	L	T	C	C	A	D	N
D	T	L	R	S	H	E	S	U	A	I	O	N	T	E	T	S	P	R	R	W
S	V	X	D	A	E	N	O	T	S	D	O	O	L	B	L	H	U	D	A	G
D	S	A	T	H	E	I	D	E	S	O	F	M	A	R	C	H	D	A	I	M
A	Y	M	E	O	C	D	N	R	T	A	E	I	S	H	L	O	U	A	E	A
Y	N	R	B	T	Y	I	S	E	F	C	E	Q	U	I	N	O	X	D	Y	O

Number Jig

9			8	7	2		2	
4	1	1	8		5		2	
0			9	4	2	3	0	4
2			2		0			0
4	1	2	2		4	7	7	2
6		2			2			4
7	2	1	0	4	7		4	
		6		6			7	
		3	8	2	5	6	5	7

Linkword

SACK, HEAT, LOAN, LION, SAIL, CAKE, BEAT **CHALICE**

Sudoku

2	5	1	3	4	8	9	7	6
7	9	8	6	5	2	3	1	4
4	3	6	7	9	1	5	8	2
6	1	3	2	7	4	8	9	5
5	2	4	8	1	9	6	3	7
8	7	9	5	6	3	2	4	1
3	4	7	9	2	5	1	6	8
9	6	2	1	8	7	4	5	3
1	8	5	4	3	6	7	2	9

Short Code

H	I	S	S	■	S	I	T	E
U	■	■	T	■	H	■	H	■
T	R	E	A	S	U	R	E	■
■	A	■	M	■	T	■	I	■
■	I	M	M	A	T	U	R	E
■	S	■	E	■	L	■	■	A
L	E	E	R	■	E	M	I	T

M	S	U	A	E
R	L	H	I	T

Brickwork

GOSPEL
SLOPE
SOLE
LOS
SLOT
STOLE
HOSTEL

Add Up

73

Suko

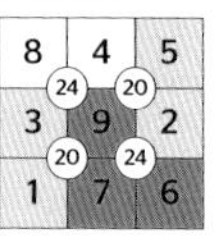

Wordsearch

E	V	I	T	I	S	O	P	O	D
Y	F	W	N	E	D	W	U	L	N
N	S	H	T	M	G	T	A	M	P
E	C	A	H	I	A	R	R	T	A
U	I	O	N	G	U	Y	U	L	T
T	T	L	E	O	G	C	I	S	L
R	A	N	M	R	D	V	R	S	O
A	T	O	E	P	E	E	C	I	V
L	S	N	E	A	R	T	H	D	C
R	E	E	S	U	F	A	I	N	S

Traffic Lights

Word Ladder

CARD, hard, hark, hack, heck, neck, DECK

Sudoku

4	6	5	7	3	1	9	2	8
9	3	1	2	8	4	6	7	5
8	2	7	9	5	6	3	4	1
1	7	6	8	9	5	4	3	2
3	9	2	1	4	7	5	8	6
5	4	8	3	6	2	7	1	9
2	5	3	6	7	8	1	9	4
7	8	4	5	1	9	2	6	3
6	1	9	4	2	3	8	5	7

Suguru

4	2	4	3	5	2	1
5	1	5	2	1	3	4
3	2	3	4	5	2	1
4	1	5	2	3	4	3
3	2	3	1	5	2	1
5	4	5	4	3	4	3
1	2	1	2	1	2	1

Solutions

Arroword

St David's Day

Kids' Corner

Honeycomb

1 Awhile 2 Mobile 3 Tidier 4 Higher 5 Bisque 6 Accrue 7 Redeem 8 Diadem 9 Ghosts 10 Squats 11 Cradle 12 Castle 13 Decide 14 Accord 15 Occurs 16 Umbria 17 Ambled 18 Squirt 19 Dither 20 Roster 21 Rushed 22 Ironed 23 Elated 24 Risked 25 Though 26 Splint 27 Splash 28 Oppugn 29 Applet 30 Squawk 31 Guilty 32 Nicety 33 Sample 34 Gurgle 35 Elvers 36 Wavers 37 Infill 38 Caddie 39 Madcap 40 Racing 41 Vacate 42 Voyage 43 Liking 44 Idling 45 Acquit 46 Nitwit 47 Tabled 48 Gained 49 Livery 50 Quarry 51 Twerps 52 Bleeps 53 Arcane 54 Ermine.

Two for Tea

Battleships

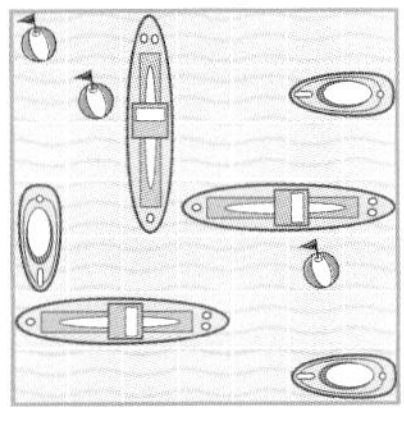

Jumbo Codeword

M	Y	Q	O	E	Z	J	U	N	W	K	T	H
X	S	P	L	F	C	V	B	D	I	A	G	R

Eiffel Tower

Roundabout

RADIAL: 1 Spoof 2 Fable 3 Facet 4 Treat 5 Trade 6 Asset 7 Sheet 8 Eddie 9 Spade 10 Erupt 11 Fibre 12 On air 13 Rings 14 Actor 15 Prior 16 Solar 17 Swear 18 Adder 19 Reins 20 Elton 21 Aisle 22 Stare 23 Erect 24 Foray.

CIRCULAR: 1 Set 4 Teases 13 Soft 16 Spa 19 SAS 20 Nasty 25 Plead 26 Shipping 27 Crowd 28 Action 29 Bore 30 Cease 31 Daub 32 Anti 33 Led 34 Asti 35 Roared 36 Rio 37 Lea 38 Ferret.

Logic Problem

Since the second person borrowed the biography (clue 6), from clue 1, a biography cannot have been brought back by the first visitor, nor can Josephine, who returned the travel book, have been there first (clue 5). The fifth arrival brought back the romance (clue 7), and clue 4 tells us the first visitor did not return the mystery novel, so, by elimination, she must have brought back the classic, and therefore took out the romance (clue 3). She is not Kelly, who took out the mystery (clue 4), nor can she be Josephine (clue 5), while Diana arrived fourth (clue 2). Clue 3 rules out Jean as the first arrival, who must therefore have been Marianne. Therefore Josephine must have arrived second (clue 5), so she must have exchanged her travel book for a biography. Jean did not arrive third (clue 3), so she must have been the fifth visitor, who returned the romance. This leaves the third arrival as Kelly. Since she took out a mystery, she cannot have returned one (intro), so, by elimination, she must have brought back a biography, leaving the mystery as the book returned by Diana. Now, from clue 1, we can see that it must have been the fourth visitor, Diana, who borrowed a classic, which leaves the travel book as the one borrowed by Jean.

In summary: Diana, fourth, mystery, classic. Jean, fifth, romance, travel. Josephine, second, travel, biography. Kelly, third, biography, mystery. Marianne, first, classic, romance.

Pathfinder

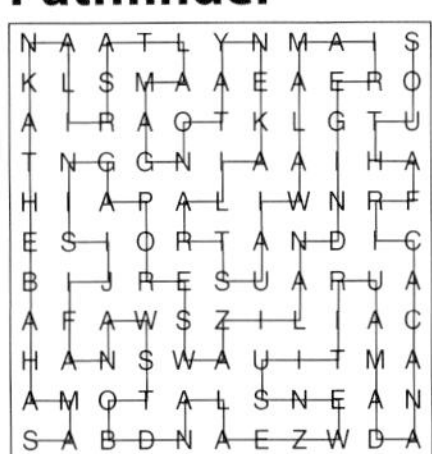

April

Oh, to be in England
Now that April's there,
And whoever wakes in England
Sees, some morning, unaware,
That the lowest boughs and the brushwood sheaf
Round the elm-tree bole are in tiny leaf,
While the chaffinch sings on the orchard bough
In England - now!

Home-Thoughts, from Abroad, by Robert Browning

Wordsearch

Find all the listed words associated with spring cleaning.

AIRING
APRON
BROOM CUPBOARD
BRUSH
BUBBLES
BUFF
CHORES
CLEANING
CLEAR-OUT
CLOTH
CLUTTER
DUSTING
ELBOW GREASE
FOAM
FRAGRANT
FRESH
FURNITURE POLISH
GLEAM
HOUSEWORK
HYGIENIC
KITCHEN
LATHER
LIMESCALE
MOP
NEAT
ORDERLY
OVEN CLEANER
OVERALLS
PAIL
PRISTINE
RINSE
RUBBER GLOVES
SCOUR
SCRUB
SHEEN
SHINE
SKIRTING-BOARD
SOAK
SPARKLE
SPICK AND SPAN
SPONGE
SPRAY
SPRING-CLEAN
STAIN REMOVAL
SUDS
SWEEP
TIDY
VACUUM
WASH UP
WIPE

WEDNESDAY
1

THURSDAY *MAUNDY THURSDAY*
2

FRIDAY *GOOD FRIDAY*
3

SATURDAY
4

SUNDAY *EASTER SUNDAY*
5

MONDAY *EASTER MONDAY*
6

TUESDAY
7

WEDNESDAY
8

Suko

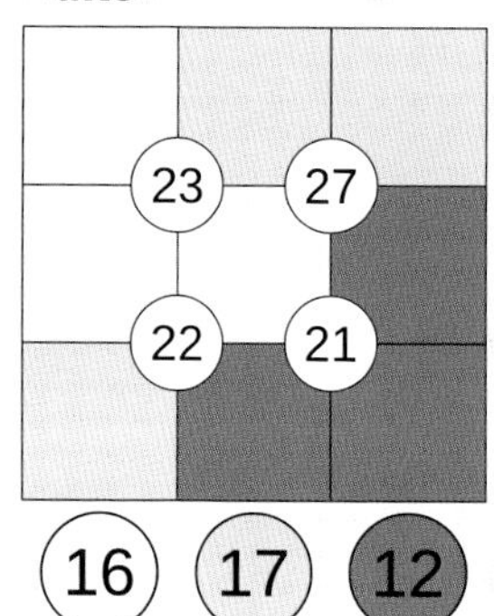

Wordsearch

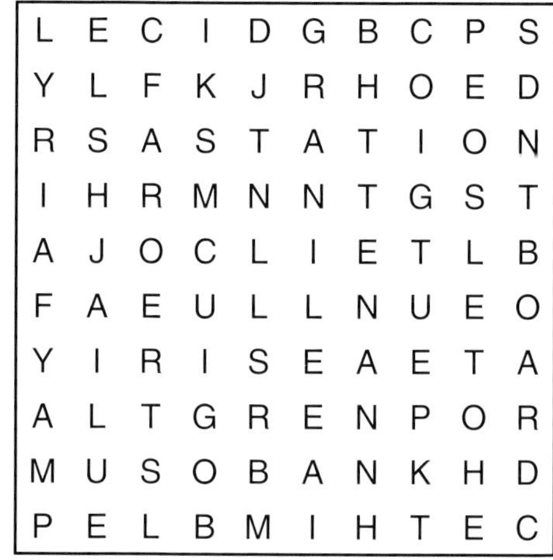

BANK	DOG	PALL MALL
BOARD	HOTEL	RENT
BOOT	HOUSE	STATION
CHANCE	JAIL	THIMBLE
DICE	MAYFAIR	UTILITIES

Sudoku

	3						8	
5		9		4		1		7
			1	7	8			
		3	2		9	7		
2	4						5	1
9			5		4			8
		7	3		5	4		
	2	4				3	7	
3								2

THURSDAY
9

FRIDAY
10

SATURDAY
11

SUNDAY
12

MONDAY
13

TUESDAY
14

WEDNESDAY
15

THURSDAY
16

Number Jig

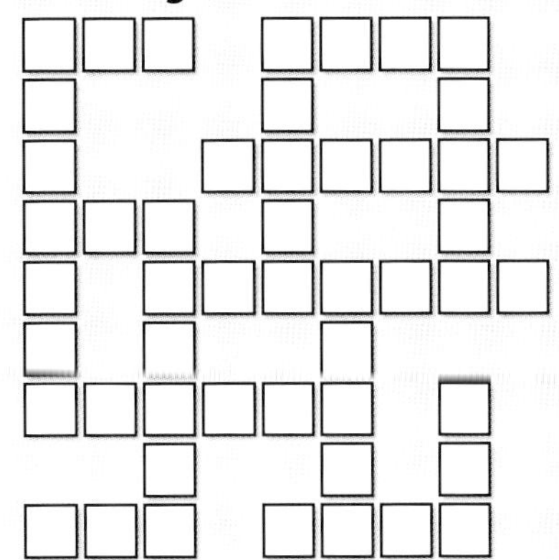

3 digits
282
302
308
486

4 digits
6746
8732

5 digits
32027
61746
66053

6 digits
173305
217788
537180

7 digits
1263838
4263345

Short Code

Safecracker

To open the safe, all 20 of the buttons must be pressed in the correct order (which is indicated by the numbers and directions on the buttons eg 2D = Two Down) before the 'open' button is pressed. What is the first button pressed in your sequence?

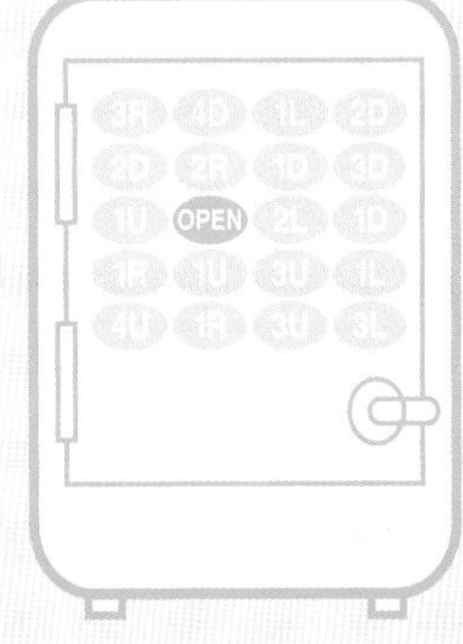

FRIDAY
17

SATURDAY
18

SUNDAY
19

MONDAY
20

TUESDAY
21

WEDNESDAY
22

THURSDAY *ST GEORGE'S DAY*
23

FRIDAY
24

Linkword

PUB					SHOW
PROFESSIONAL					PLAY
GOING					ACTION
ARUM					PAD
COSMIC					JACKET
POTTING					TEARS
FRONT					HANDLE

Sudoku

		6						
			8					7
1		7			6	9	4	
	8			3			6	4
			7		4			
		3		5			2	
		2					7	
		4	9		1	8		
	3		4					

Brickwork

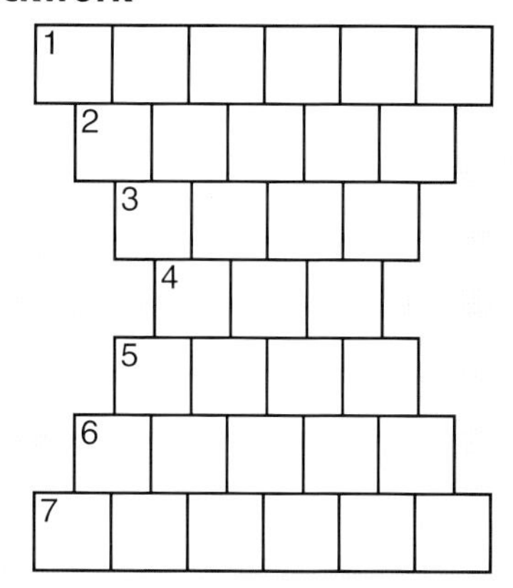

1 Ship unloader (6)
2 Interior design (5)
3 Thick string (4)
4 Fishing-pole (3)
5 Part of a sentence (4)
6 Perish at sea (5)
7 Ask oneself (6)

SATURDAY
25

SUNDAY
26

MONDAY
27

TUESDAY
28

WEDNESDAY
29

THURSDAY
30

NOTES

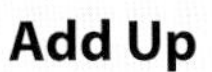

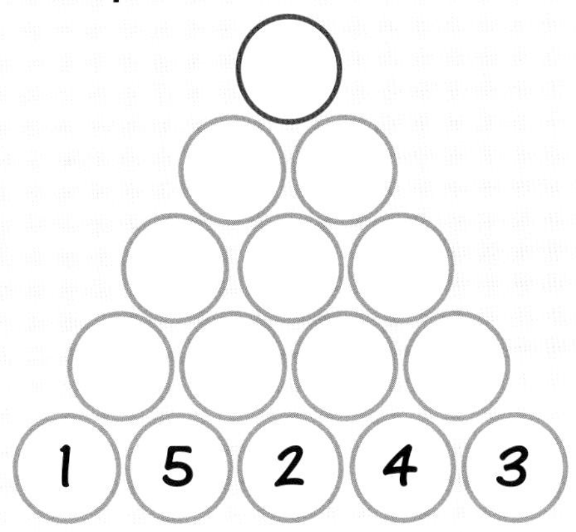

Word Ladder

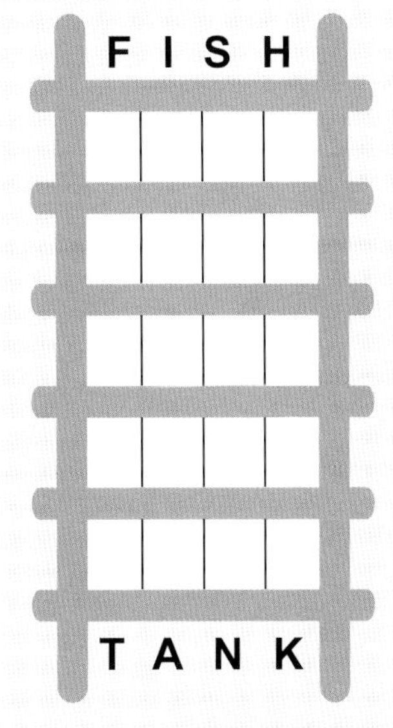

Suguru

2		5				
	3				3	1
		5	4			
				2		
	4		4			2

Crossword

The shaded squares will spell out the name of a famous writer born in April.

ACROSS

1 Hit with an open hand (4)
6 Beautiful white bird (pictured) (4)
8 Southern US state (7)
9 Shed tears (3)
11 Bone of the torso (3)
13 End, finish (5)
16 Roll of tobacco leaves for smoking (5)
18 Astonish (5)
19 Makes corrections to (text) (5)
20 Noise made by a horse (5)
21 Light sailing vessel (5)
22 Caress with the lips (4)
25 Part of speech with tenses (4)
27 Extremely thin pastry (4)
28 Burglar's loot (4)
29 On guard, cautious (4)
31 Slope from one level to another (4)
34 Bubbly (drink) (5)
37 Enthusiastic, keen (5)
38 Kick out of school (5)
39 Just right (5)
40 Skin on top of the head (5)
43 Money pouch (5)
46 Horoscope lion (3)
49 Hardened, like cement (3)
50 Substance used for injections against disease (7)
51 Newcastle's river (4)
52 Part of a ladder (4)

DOWN

2 Shoe-tie (4)
3 Settles a bill (4)
4 Container for shopping (3)
5 Dried grass (3)
6 Indian dress (4)
7 Swedish pop group (4)
10 Bone in the forearm (6)
12 Put a light to (6)
13 Nerve, impudence (5)
14 Uncomplicated (4)
15 White after-bath powder (4)
16 Hundredth part of a dollar (4)
17 Course of therapy following addiction or illness (5)
23 Balearic island (5)
24 Short literary work (5)
25 Movable part of a helmet, that covers the face (5)
26 Kingdom (5)
29 Periods of time (5)
30 West Indian-style music (6)
32 Have high hopes (6)
33 Regular beat of the heart (5)
34 Hold tightly (4)
35 Look for (4)
36 Sharp or high-pitched bark (4)
41 Material used in pottery (4)
42 Tennis score of zero (4)
44 One who consumes or operates (4)
45 Render senseless with a blow (4)
47 Make a move (3)
48 Flan (3)

Jigword

3 letters
FAT
FRY
JAB
JAR
PIT
ROC
TAW
YAP

4 letters
AQUA
FREE
HUSS
IOWA
LARD
OUST
UPON
WIFE

5 letters
BOSSY
DRAWL
ENSUE
LOYAL
MAMBA
MASON
NOOSE
SMEAR
STUMP
UDDER

6 letters
ABSORB
AMENDS
CANVAS
DEFEND
EMBARK
HATBOX
MYRIAD
ROADIE

7 letters
BENEFIT
EARACHE
ELITIST
ETERNAL
EXCLUDE
EXPOUND
FULSOME
RAILWAY
RIOTOUS
ROLLMOP
SABBATH
SKITTER
SLATTED

8 letters
DEFRAYAL
ENCUMBER
GYMKHANA
~~MARATHON~~
UNIVERSE

9 letters
FANATICAL
ILLOGICAL
INTERVIEW
SLINGSHOT
TORTUROUS

10 letters
RETROSPECT

11 letters
LEISUREWEAR
MATRIARCHAL
PROHIBITIVE

Drop Zone

Seven columns, or stacks of lettered balls - remove a ball and the others above it will drop down in its place. Your task is to remove one ball from each column so that when all the other balls drop down, they will spell out six words reading across. What are they, and what word will be spelled out by the seven balls you remove?

Two Timer

Two sets of clues to the same answers.

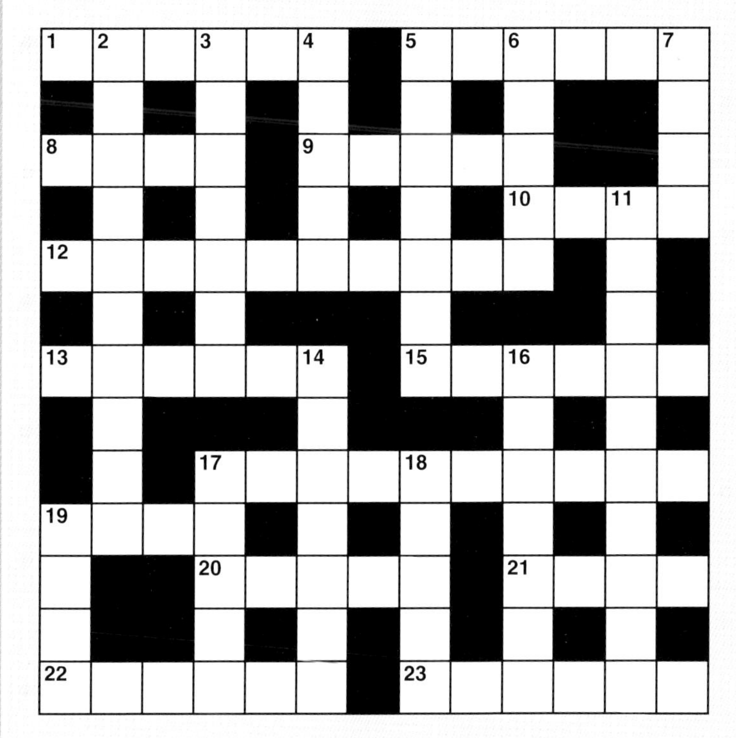

STRAIGHT CLUES

ACROSS

1 Arrow's feathered end (6)
5 ___ beer, fizzy spicy drink (6)
8 Declare to be true (4)
9 Made regular journeys (5)
10 Irritating sensation (4)
12 Acting secretly (10)
13 Savage and ruthless (6)
15 Use of force to procure something (6)
17 Person who prepares text for printing (10)
19 Bullets or shells, colloquially (4)
20 Clinically overweight (5)
21 Metal fastener (4)
22 System of procedure (6)
23 Vow, assurance (6)

DOWN

2 Sitting area in a house (6,4)
3 Article of dress (7)
4 Theme to talk or write about (5)
5 Lamented (7)
6 Point in the heavens opposite the zenith (5)
7 Possessing great wealth (4)
11 Mortifying (10)
14 Understand by following mouth movements (3-4)
16 Group of aides travelling with a VIP (7)
17 Canine or molar, for example (5)
18 Person who cleans chimneys (5)
19 Nucleus and its electrons (4)

CRYPTIC CLUES

ACROSS

1 It may come before and after landing (6)
5 Redheaded group (6)
8 Some have reason to assert (4)
9 Penny was not honest about having worked steadily (5)
10 Italian child's restless desire (4)
12 Protected indoors (10)
13 Inhuman but about right with a beginner (6)
15 Constraint sees union leader put in robe (6)
17 Peter testy about printer (10)
19 Nameless Egyptian god's explosive devices (4)
20 See another old boy first who's corpulent (5)
21 Tack removing head of garden pest (4)
22 Bumped into brick carrier making way (6)
23 Promise toast (6)

DOWN

2 Existing accommodation? (6,4)
3 Grant me replacement clothing (7)
4 Subject to photo briefly? (5)
5 Lady stuck in grating felt sorrow (7)
6 A rind developed at the bottom (5)
7 Wealthy have religious instruction before church (4)
11 Moderating effect of the canings administered (10)
14 Not a sound way to see what another says (3-4)
16 Entourage mutineer riotously but not to start with (7)
17 Saw part of canine perhaps (5)
18 Not much between the odds in gamble (5)
19 Small part of first half of alphabet (4)

Quiz Wordsearch

Answer the given clues and then find the answers hidden in the grid.

K X L U L V T T N A N N E T D I V A D F C
L U S E R I B A E E N C H A N T E D L G I
L G S K R C E P X E E Y U E L S R A O U N
O I Y E R T S E O Y M T I L G F N O S S A
B E A C R O E H S U E M T P I O D O I M T
T E D P L R N C R E I A A E I F S O R A I
T Y S E C I L R A G N S R T R M I L A S T
S K E H E A O U T R S R A I H F O N P T E
B I G L P B S O E O T N D A C O D T N E R
F N R I E E S L V O D A H G F M M N I R H
T U O A R C E E N N Y D O I Y S E P U S O
C A E L R K R T A P D N I B E A B S S A O
R E G T H H U R L U D N O M A I D I G O L
N M T A E A G C B S K V O R T I A E N F N
L S S R E M O C H A R L I E C H A P L I N

1 _ *April*, 1991 Joan Plowright film (9)

2 Annual Aintree steeplechase (5,8)

3 Annual event on the Thames (4,4)

4 *April* _, Ella Fitzgerald song (2,5)

5 *April* _, Patti Smith song (4)

6 April 23 commemoration (2,7,3)

7 British liner which sank on 15th April 1912 (7)

8 Commemoration of the Crucifixion (4,6)

9 Golf tournament held in Augusta (2,7)

10 Major religion founder whose birthday is celebrated on 8th April (6)

11 *Nanny McPhee* star whose birthday is 15th April (4,8)

12 One half of a celebrity couple celebrating her birthday on 17th April (8,7)

13 Pesach (8)

14 Place to get your clothes washed, the first in Britain opened on 18th April 1934 (11)

15 Precious stone, birthstone for April (7)

16 Silent-film actor who was born 16th April 1889 (7,7)

17 TV's tenth Doctor Who whose birthday is 18th April (5,7)

18 Twelve-month period beginning on April 6 (3,4)

Logic Problem

Four aspiring British actresses have been filling in their time by doing 'extra' work at the famous Larchwood Studios and each makes her first appearance on screen in a newly released movie. From the clues given below, can you work out how long each of them appears in the film, the role she's playing and the title of the movie?

Clues

1 The name of the actress seen (fleetingly) in *Plain Clothes* immediately follows in the alphabetical list that of the one who is on screen for 47 seconds as a hospital nurse.

2 Donna Essex, who plays a cab driver – one of a large number of motorists caught in a traffic jam – is visible for a shorter period than the actress who's an extra in *Bad Company*.

3 Angie Bruce makes the shortest screen appearance of all, but not as a uniformed air hostess.

4 No receptionist appears, however briefly, in the foreground or the background, in *High Flyers*.

	17 seconds	29 seconds	47 seconds	54 seconds	Air hostess	Cab driver	Nurse	Receptionist	*Bad Company*	*Green Sun*	*High Flyers*	*Plain Clothes*
Angie Bruce												
Donna Essex												
Gail Hatton												
Julie Kirby												
Bad Company												
Green Sun												
High Flyers												
Plain Clothes												
Air hostess												
Cab driver												
Nurse												
Receptionist												

Actress	Screen time	Role	Film

Jolly Mixtures

ACROSS
1 ARCHAISM
6 PAWS
8 SIRI
9 ERITREAN
10 LYRE
11 ECARTE
13 HOLT
15 PANES
17 PEERS
19 ACRE
21 SPADES
24 A LOP
26 FINE MALT
27 ITEM
28 MARY
29 DEMURRED

DOWN
2 HEROD
3 TERSELY
4 ARTIST
5 TACIT
6 A VIEW
7 RESPECT
12 SIRE
14 CONE
16 CARRIES
18 GET ROPE
20 NECTAR
22 SAMEY
23 ARMED
25 VELIA

Solutions

Wordsearch

F	R	E	S	H	M	A	O	F	S	E	V	O	L	G	R	E	B	B	U	R
N	E	E	H	S	D	T	Y	L	I	A	P	D	T	C	D	T	M	T	Y	D
L	Y	D	T	I	E	T	I	R	M	E	D	O	T	L	I	A	E	E	U	E
O	A	A	A	L	S	K	I	R	T	I	N	G	B	O	A	R	D	S	L	P
W	T	T	R	O	O	N	I	Y	E	D	A	M	O	T	E	I	T	A	T	I
N	A	E	H	P	S	V	R	E	T	T	U	L	C	H	M	I	V	O	I	W
C	H	O	R	E	S	B	E	T	S	S	F	S	N	T	N	O	E	D	P	S
A	S	H	T	R	R	R	E	N	U	A	C	F	U	G	M	V	P	U	P	H
O	W	A	I	U	N	O	M	D	C	O	E	O	U	E	L	A	H	I	T	Y
N	E	M	E	T	E	O	S	U	U	L	R	R	R	B	F	S	C	O	S	G
N	E	I	O	I	H	M	S	R	U	A	E	N	G	Y	A	K	A	P	E	I
T	P	C	R	N	C	C	D	E	E	C	I	A	N	W	A	T	R	L	H	E
E	N	A	D	R	T	U	L	L	L	A	A	I	N	N	O	I	O	S	E	N
N	T	A	E	U	I	P	C	E	T	B	E	V	D	E	N	B	L	W	N	I
A	H	G	R	F	K	B	A	S	A	L	B	S	S	G	R	L	L	B	I	C
G	S	N	L	G	I	O	M	P	E	N	P	U	C	P	A	O	U	E	T	C
D	U	I	Y	N	A	A	T	R	R	A	I	L	B	R	A	R	T	A	S	S
E	R	R	I	S	H	R	L	I	N	O	E	N	E	O	C	R	E	A	I	H
N	B	I	R	T	Y	D	F	I	D	A	N	V	G	S	S	E	K	F	R	I
S	O	A	K	M	A	E	L	G	N	Y	O	S	P	O	N	G	E	L	P	N
C	K	R	O	W	E	S	U	O	H	L	I	M	E	S	C	A	L	E	E	E

Number Jig

4	8	6		6	7	4	6	
2				1			6	
6			1	7	3	3	0	5
3	0	2		4			5	
3		1	2	6	3	8	3	8
4		7			2			
5	3	7	1	8	0		2	
		8			2		8	
3	0	8		8	7	3	2	

Linkword

QUIZ, FOUL, LIVE, LILY, DUST, SHED, DOOR **QUILTED**

Sudoku

8	4	6	1	9	7	2	5	3
3	2	9	8	4	5	6	1	7
1	5	7	3	2	6	9	4	8
7	8	1	2	3	9	5	6	4
2	6	5	7	1	4	3	8	9
4	9	3	6	5	8	7	2	1
9	1	2	5	8	3	4	7	6
5	7	4	9	6	1	8	3	2
6	3	8	4	7	2	1	9	5

Short Code

P	I	F	W	A
G	N	R	T	E

Brickwork

DOCKER
DECOR
CORD
ROD
WORD
DROWN
WONDER

Add Up

52

Suko

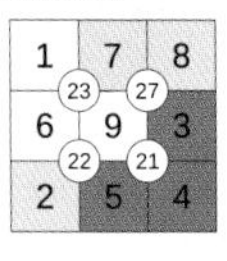

Wordsearch

L	E	C	I	D	G	B	C	P	S
Y	L	F	K	J	R	H	O	E	D
R	S	A	S	T	A	T	I	O	N
I	H	R	M	N	N	T	G	S	T
A	J	O	C	L	I	E	T	L	B
F	A	E	U	L	L	N	U	E	O
Y	I	R	I	S	E	A	E	T	A
A	L	T	G	R	E	N	P	O	R
M	U	S	O	B	A	N	K	H	D
P	E	L	B	M	I	H	T	E	C

Safecracker

3R	4D	1L	2D
2D	2R	1D	3D
1U	OPEN	2L	1D
1R	1U	3U	1L
4U	1R	3U	3L

Word Ladder

FISH, dish, dash, cash, cask, task, TANK

Sudoku

7	3	1	9	5	2	6	8	4
5	8	9	6	4	3	1	2	7
4	6	2	1	7	8	5	9	3
1	5	3	2	8	9	7	4	6
2	4	8	7	3	6	9	5	1
9	7	6	5	1	4	2	3	8
8	1	7	3	2	5	4	6	9
6	2	4	8	9	1	3	7	5
3	9	5	4	6	7	8	1	2

Suguru

1	4	1	3	4	2	1
2	3	5	2	1	3	4
5	1	4	3	4	5	2
2	3	2	1	2	3	1
5	1	5	4	5	4	5
2	3	2	3	2	3	1
1	4	1	4	1	5	2

Solutions

Crossword

S	L	A	P	■	B	■	H	■	S	W	A	N
■	A	■	A	L	A	B	A	M	A	■	B	■
■	C	R	Y	■	G	■	Y	■	R	I	B	■
C	E	A	S	E	■	T	■	C	I	G	A	R
H	■	D	■	A	M	A	Z	E	■	N	■	E
E	D	I	T	S	■	L	■	N	E	I	G	H
E	■	U	■	Y	A	C	H	T	■	T	■	A
K	I	S	S						V	E	R	B
■	B	■	T						I	■	E	■
F	I	L	O						S	W	A	G
■	Z	■	R						O	■	L	■
W	A	R	Y						R	A	M	P
E	■	E	■	G	A	S	S	Y	■	S	■	U
E	A	G	E	R	■	E	■	E	X	P	E	L
K	■	G	■	I	D	E	A	L	■	I	■	S
S	C	A	L	P	■	K	■	P	U	R	S	E
■	L	E	O	■	A	■	P	■	S	E	T	■
■	A	■	V	A	C	C	I	N	E	■	U	■
T	Y	N	E	■	T	■	E	■	R	U	N	G

Shakespeare

Quiz Wordsearch

K	X	L	U	L	V	T	T	N	A	N	N	E	T	D	I	V	A	D	F	C
L	U	S	E	R	I	B	A	E	E	N	C	H	A	N	T	E	D	L	G	I
L	G	S	K	R	C	E	P	X	E	E	Y	U	E	L	S	R	A	O	U	N
O	I	Y	E	R	T	S	E	O	Y	M	T	I	L	G	F	N	O	S	S	A
B	E	A	C	R	O	E	H	S	U	E	M	T	P	I	O	D	O	I	M	T
T	E	D	P	L	R	N	C	R	E	I	A	A	E	I	F	S	O	R	A	I
T	Y	S	E	C	I	L	R	A	G	N	S	R	T	R	M	I	L	A	S	T
S	K	E	H	E	A	O	U	T	R	S	R	A	I	H	E	O	N	P	T	E
B	I	G	L	P	B	S	O	E	O	T	N	D	A	C	O	D	T	N	E	R
F	N	R	I	E	E	S	L	V	O	D	A	H	G	F	M	M	N	I	R	H
T	U	O	A	R	C	E	E	N	N	Y	D	O	I	Y	S	E	P	U	S	O
C	A	E	L	R	K	R	T	A	P	D	N	I	B	E	A	B	S	S	A	O
R	E	G	T	H	H	U	R	L	U	D	N	O	M	A	I	D	I	G	O	L
N	M	T	A	E	A	G	C	B	S	K	V	O	R	T	I	A	E	N	F	N
L	S	S	R	E	M	O	C	H	A	R	L	I	E	C	H	A	P	L	I	N

1 *ENCHANTED*
2 GRAND NATIONAL
3 BOAT RACE
4 *IN PARIS*
5 *FOOL*
6 ST GEORGE'S DAY
7 TITANIC
8 GOOD FRIDAY
9 US MASTERS
10 BUDDHA
11 EMMA THOMPSON
12 VICTORIA BECKHAM
13 PASSOVER
14 LAUNDERETTE
15 DIAMOND
16 CHARLIE CHAPLIN
17 DAVID TENNANT
18 TAX YEAR

Jigword

Drop Zone

S	H	A	L	L	O	W
K	N	I	T	T	E	D
C	R	U	M	B	L	E
A	N	T	L	E	R	S
B	E	A	C	H	E	D
M	A	G	N	I	F	Y
P	O	L	I	T	I	C

Two Timer

ACROSS: 1 Flight 5 Ginger 8 Aver 9 Plied 10 Itch 12 Undercover 13 Brutal 15 Duress 17 Typesetter 19 Ammo 20 Obese 21 Nail 22 Method 23 Pledge.

DOWN: 2 Living room 3 Garment 4 Topic 5 Grieved 6 Nadir 7 Rich 11 Chastening 14 Lip-read 16 Retinue 17 Tooth 18 Sweep 19 Atom.

Logic Problem

Angie Bruce is on screen for 17 seconds (clue 3) and the actress playing the nurse for 47 seconds (clue 1), so Donna Essex, who appears as a cab driver for less than 54 seconds (clue 2), must be on screen for 29 seconds. We know that the nurse who's seen for 47 seconds isn't Angie Bruce or Donna Essex, nor can she be Julie Kirby (clue 1), so she must be Gail Hatton, and, from clue 1, Julie Kirby must be in *Plain Clothes*. By elimination, she must appear for 54 seconds. Therefore, from clue 2, Gail Hatton's 47-second appearance as a nurse must be in *Bad Company*. Angie Bruce's 17-second role isn't as an air hostess (clue 3), so must be as a receptionist, and the air hostess must be Julie Kirby. Finally, from clue 4, Angie Bruce's appearance isn't in *High Flyers*, so must be in *Green Sun*, and it's *High Flyers* in which Donna Essex appears for 29 seconds as a cab driver.

In summary: Angie Bruce, 17 seconds, receptionist, *Green Sun*. Donna Essex, 29 seconds, cab driver, *High Flyers*. Gail Hatton, 47 seconds, nurse, *Bad Company*. Julie Kirby, 54 seconds, air hostess, *Plain Clothes*.

Jolly Mixtures

The wind at North and East
Was never good for man nor beast
So never think to cast a clout
Until the month of May be out

From F. K. Robertson's 'Whitby Gazette', 1855

Wordsearch

Find all the listed words and phrases associated with May, together with stars celebrating their birthdays this month, hidden in the grid.

BELTANE
BONO
CHEESE ROLLING
CHELSEA FLOWER SHOW
DAVID BECKHAM
EMERALD
ETA AQUARIDS
EUROVISION SONG CONTEST
FA CUP FINAL
GEMINI
GEORGE CLOONEY
HAY FESTIVAL
HELENA BONHAM CARTER
KYLIE MINOGUE
LILY OF THE VALLEY
MAIA
MAY DAY
MAY QUEEN
MAYPOLE
PARADE
TAURUS
VE DAY

FRIDAY
1

SATURDAY
2

SUNDAY
3

MONDAY *EARLY MAY BANK HOLIDAY*
4

TUESDAY
5

WEDNESDAY
6

THURSDAY
7

FRIDAY
8

Suko

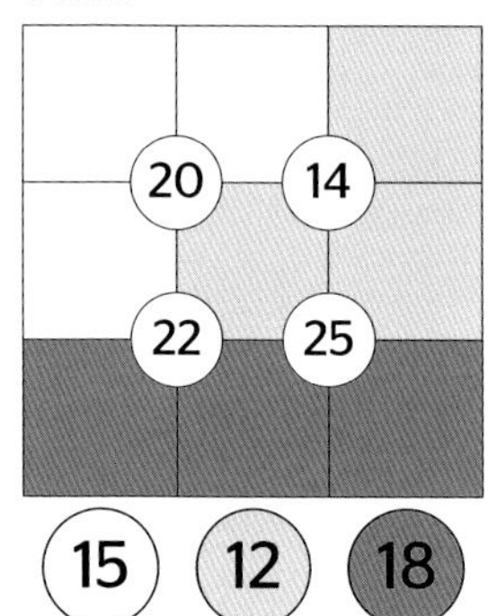

Wordsearch

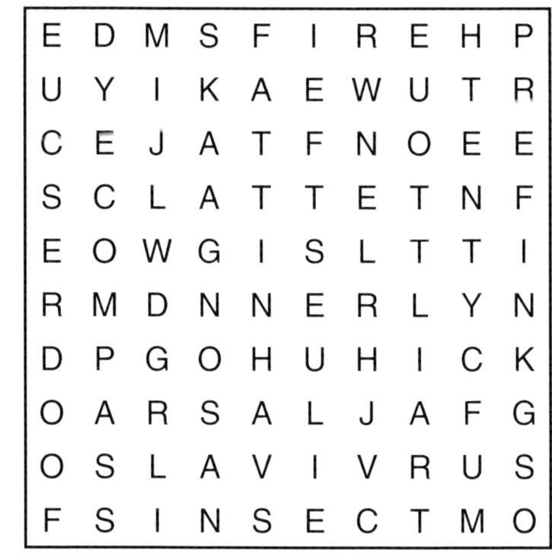

E	D	M	S	F	I	R	E	H	P
U	Y	I	K	A	E	W	U	T	R
C	E	J	A	T	F	N	O	E	E
S	C	L	A	T	T	E	T	N	F
E	O	W	G	I	S	L	T	T	I
R	M	D	N	N	E	R	L	Y	N
D	P	G	O	H	U	H	I	C	K
O	A	R	S	A	L	J	A	F	G
O	S	L	A	V	I	V	R	U	S
F	S	I	N	S	E	C	T	M	O

CAVE
COMPASS
FIRE
FIRST AID
FOOD
HUNTING
INSECT
JUNGLE
KNIFE
RESCUE
SAFETY
SHELTER
SURVIVAL
TENT
WATER

Sudoku

		7						
		5	1	9			2	8
			5	8		4		9
6				2	8	9	4	
	8			5			7	
2				6	3	5	8	
			6	4		1		7
		9	3	7			6	2
		2						

SATURDAY
9

SUNDAY
10

MONDAY
11

TUESDAY
12

WEDNESDAY
13

THURSDAY
14

FRIDAY
15

SATURDAY
16

Number Jig

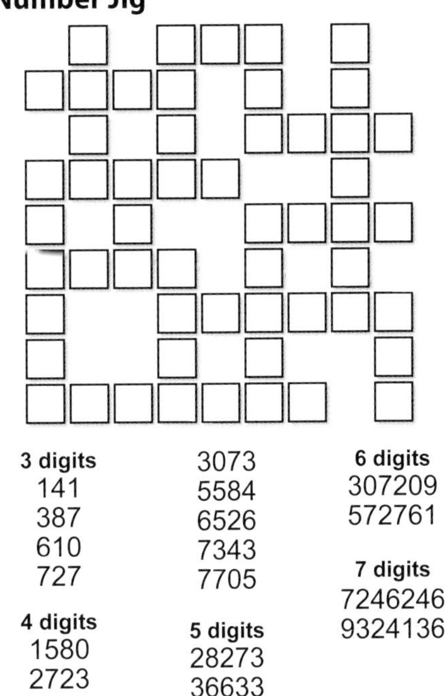

Short Code

Noughts and Crosses

The numbered squares around the edge of the grid describe the number of crosses in all the vertical, horizontal and diagonal lines connecting with that square. Complete the grid so that there is a nought or a cross in every square.

1	3	3	3	4	4	1
4						4
2		X				3
2						2
5						4
4			O			4
1	3	2	7	1	4	1

SUNDAY
17

MONDAY
18

TUESDAY
19

WEDNESDAY
20

THURSDAY
21

FRIDAY
22

SATURDAY
23

SUNDAY
24

Linkword

BROWN					CELLAR
KEEP					DOWN
FINISHING					OFFICE
FIRE					HANDLE
WEB					BOY
LOST					FOOD
SEA					SPOON

Sudoku

		5	9		4	8		
	1	2				9	4	
				3				
4			7		6			2
6								3
		4	1		9	3		
		6	3	7	5	2		
5		9				7		1

Brickwork

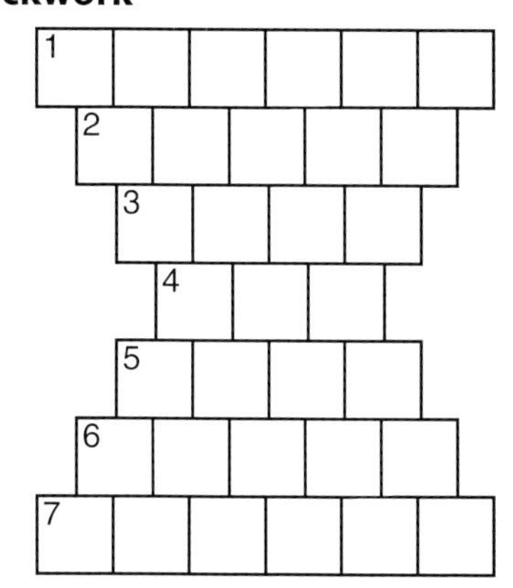

1 Mould, fungus (6)
2 Irish playwright (5)
3 Join (metal pieces) (4)
4 Showed the way (3)
5 Lazy (4)
6 Meadow (5)
7 Did not succeed (6)

MONDAY *SPRING BANK HOLIDAY*

25

TUESDAY

26

WEDNESDAY

27

THURSDAY

28

FRIDAY

29

SATURDAY

30

SUNDAY

31

Add Up

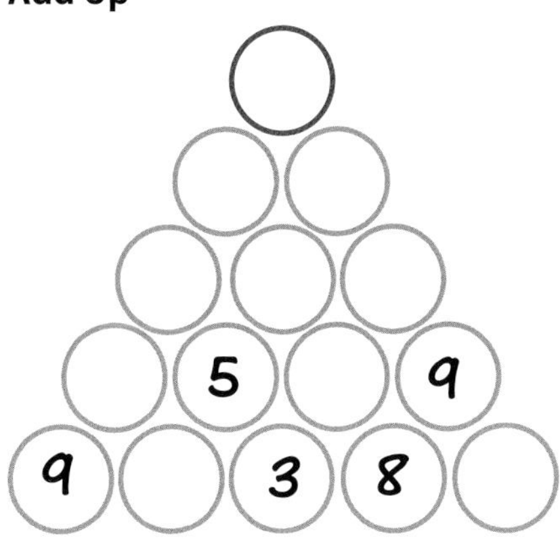

Word Ladder

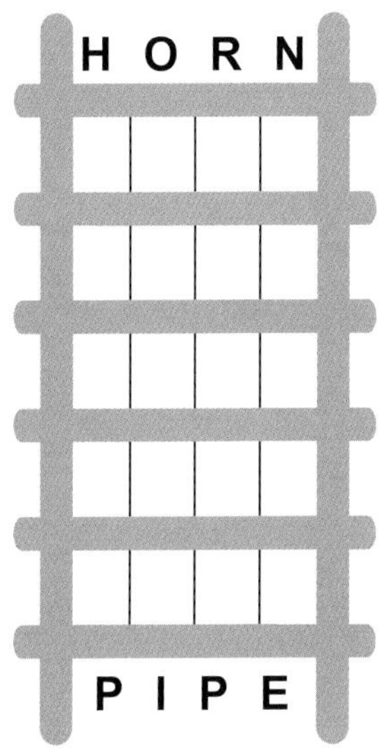

Suguru

5		4	3			
						3
					1	
			4			
				5		
		3		1		

Arroword

- Long way off
- Originators, creators
- Short-lived mania
- Punctuation mark
- Penniless
- Clinically overweight
- Arranged cutlery on (a table)
- Clean with a broom
- Deciduous tree (see picture)
- Puffed, panted
- Police, informally
- Goal, ambition
- Thought
- Sandhill
- Adult males
- Sports team
- Com-mercials, in short
- __ Peron, Madonna screen role
- Bound hand and foot (4,2)
- Sight organ
- Remove unwanted plants
- Round red-rinded Dutch cheese
- Colour-stained
- Wild drunken party
- Dotty, batty
- Lose colour and brightness
- Facts, info
- Container for return mail (inits)
- Read quickly
- Dutch shoe
- Metal pin for wood
- Angry, furious
- Applaud
- Observed (6,2)
- Rhyming verse
- Subject, theme
- Wallpaper adhesive
- Cornflakes, eg
- Lend an __, listen attentively
- Strange people
- 60 seconds
- Very strong wind
- Greatly impressive
- Alphabet character
- Revise text
- Mobile table
- Marital split
- __ Halliwell, singer
- First name of actress Ms Basinger
- Grass colour
- __ up, command to a horse
- (Of a train) came off the track
- Used a spade
- Remain
- Johnny Speight's Mr Garnett
- Move in a circle
- __ evening, tonight
- Plastic golf peg

Rearrange the shaded letters to spell out the name of an athlete who achieved a world record in May 1954.

Flight Plan

Follow the trail of each jumbo jet to discover its destination.

Honeycomb

All the answers are six-letter words. Each answer is entered in a circle around its clue number. The first letter of the answer is entered in the shaded triangle immediately above the clue number. If the clue number is odd, enter the answer in an anti-clockwise direction. If the clue number is even, enter the answer in a clockwise direction.

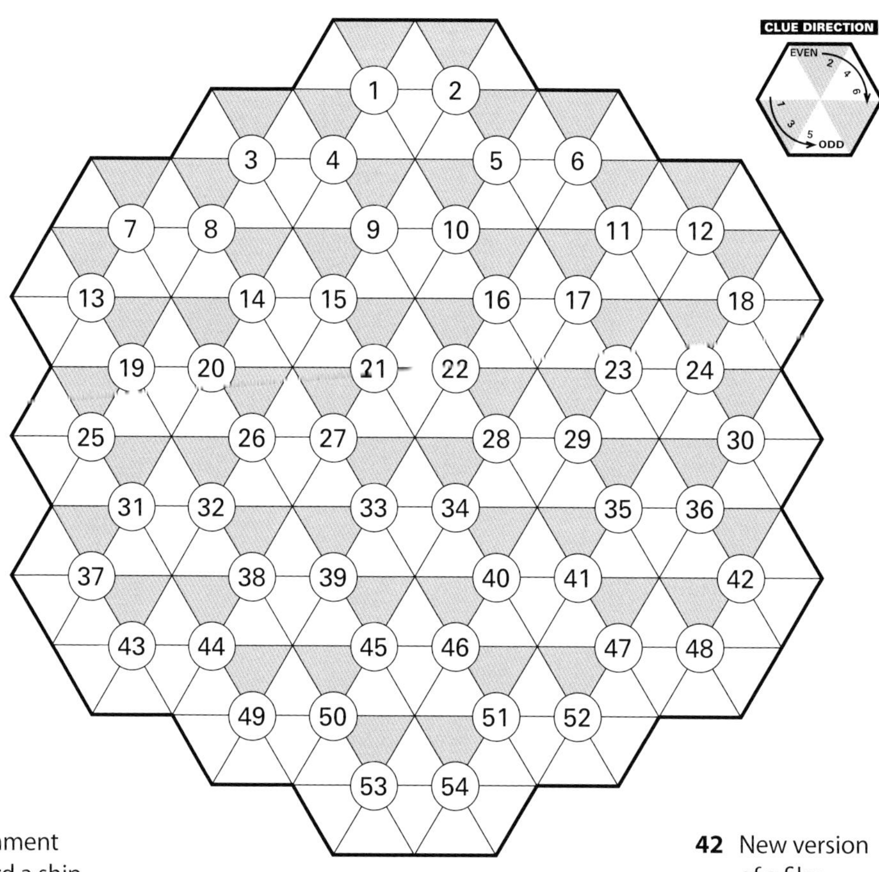

1 Comment
2 Board a ship
3 Of mixed origin
4 European capital
5 Using the oven
6 Exhausting
7 Burning brightly
8 Gentle wind
9 Storage unit
10 Assassin
11 Most mature
12 Truthful
13 Controversial Nabokov novel
14 Put up with
15 Scottish patron saint
16 Deadly
17 Small and dainty
18 Learner
19 Headings
20 Indian monetary units
21 Stoat's winter fur
22 Comedy writer and actor, Caroline
23 Bouncing *Winnie-the-Pooh* character
24 Hot coal
25 Rush of excitement
26 Splendid residence
27 African country
28 Simpler
29 Garrulous person
30 Kept on at
31 Animal bedding
32 Easy gallop
33 Guard
34 One or the other
35 Convent head
36 Way out
37 Most faithful
38 Freshest
39 Payment
40 Animal feed container
41 Irish accent
42 New version of a film
43 Ensemble of seven
44 Confidential
45 Hydrophobia
46 Scouts' sister organisation
47 More unsightly
48 German emperor
49 Throngs
50 Two-legged creatures
51 Of an engine, running slowly
52 Existing
53 Like the gates of Heaven?
54 Probable

Two for Tea

ACROSS

1 Common bird (6)
6 Ease up, lessen (5)
7 Class of animal to which humans belong (6)
9 Browse (through) a publication (5)
12 Trunk (5)
14 Finnish steam bath (5)
16 Drink to (5)
19 Starting point (6)
21 Forward (money) (5)
22 Like soil (smell or taste) (6)

DOWN

1 Entice (5)
2 Distilled drink (3)
3 Common fraction (4)
4 Salvador ___, Spanish artist (4)
5 Frail, feeble (4)
8 ___ basket, carrycot (5)
10 Rested (against) (5)
11 Metal food container (3)
13 Yoko ___, John Lennon's widow (3)
15 Suitably (5)
16 Move round, whirl (4)
17 Highest point of achievement (4)
18 On-course betting system (4)
20 Wino (3)

ACROSS

1 Ice-cream dessert (6)
6 Part of the face (5)
7 Skylighted central area of a building (6)
9 Enquired (5)
12 Buying and selling (5)
14 Sum of all amounts (5)
16 Readily available, especially of beer (2,3)
19 Strange thing (6)
21 Large coniferous tree with fragrant wood (5)
22 Personal suit-maker (6)

DOWN

1 Vertical mine entrance (5)
2 Word paired with 'neither' (3)
3 ___ Thompson, *Love Actually* actress (4)
4 ___ beds, one on top of the other (4)
5 Sound made by an object falling onto the floor (4)
8 Indira Gandhi's country (5)
10 Long sharp weapon (5)
11 Long period of time (3)
13 Make a dash for it (3)
15 Coating, tier (5)
16 That hurt! (4)
17 Neatly arranged (4)
18 Harbour, or fortified wine (4)
20 Poorly, unwell (3)

Four Square

The value of each shape is the number of sides each shape has, multiplied by the number within it. Thus a square containing the number 4 has a value of 16. Find a block of four squares (two squares wide by two squares high) with a total value of exactly 50.

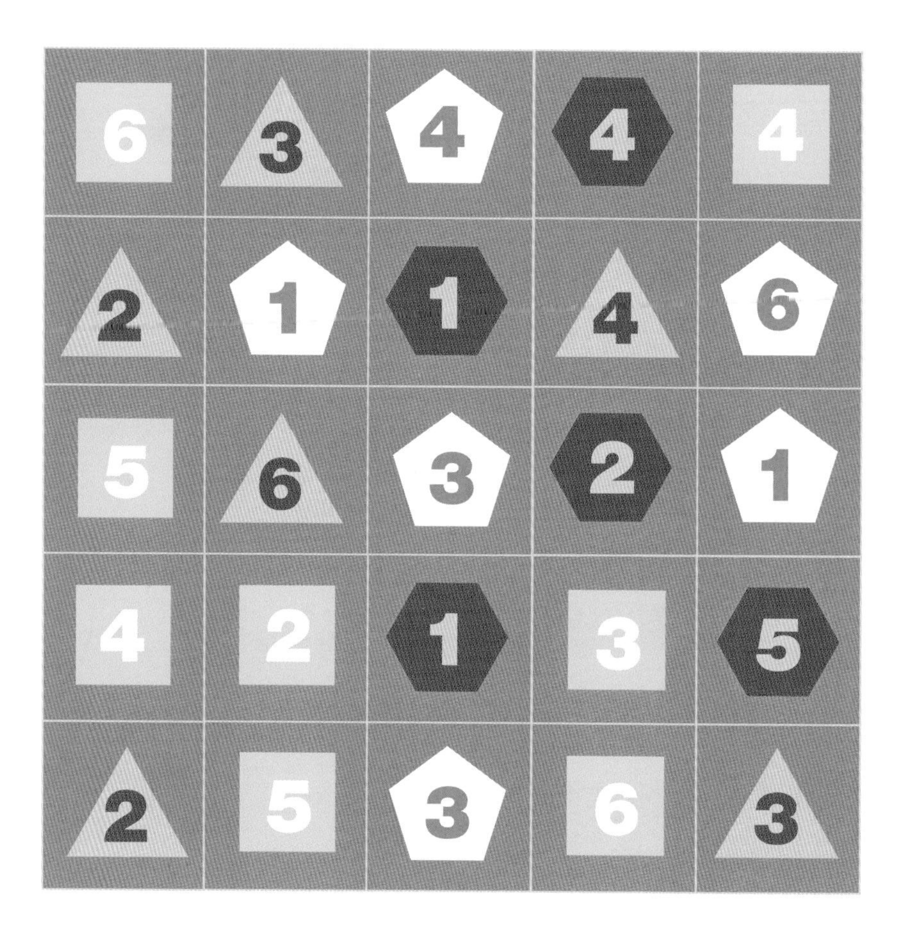

Jumbo Codeword

The letters in the phrase box will spell out the name of a woman who made history in May 1930.

3	23	9	17	14	13	13	■	9	5	4	18	22
21	■	17	■	■	23	22	11	10	■	18	■	5
6	26	18	■	23	6	21	■	21	6	6	■	9
14	■	22 R	5 U	2 G	■	17	21	21	■	23	4	17
13	18	18	■	14	■	10	21	17	■	8	■	8
26	■	21	2	8	18	■	7	■	3	21	8	18
■	11	■	22	18	4	8	18	17	18	■	23	■
9	21	26	23	■	21	■	6	■	11	■	1	■
■	24	■	17	14	11	25	■	11	10	14	18	13
■	16	■	14	■	10	14	17	■	23	■	8	■
19	5	21	17	18	■	17	21	22	24	■	8	■
■	22	■	5	■	23	■	20	■	14	17	18	3
■	18	■	6	5	11	10	18	9	9	■	6	■
14	6	8	18	■	17	■	6	21	3	18	■	18
17	■	23	■	9	21	4	■	22	■	8	23	15
9	23	20	■	21	22	18	■	22	26	18	■	11
18	■	13	8	5	■	17	22	26	■	12	14	18
8	■	5	■	17	5	17	5	■	■	18	■	18
13	14	8	17	10	■	26	18	23	22	24	18	6

A B C D E F ~~G~~ H I J K L M N O P Q ~~R~~ S T ~~U~~ V W X Y Z

1	2	3	4	5	6	7	8	9	10	11	12	13
	G			U								
14	**15**	**16**	**17**	**18**	**19**	**20**	**21**	**22**	**23**	**24**	**25**	**26**
								R				

23	3	26		16	21	10	24	9	21	24

Roundabout

Solutions to Radial clues (1 to 24) either start from the outer edge of the circle and read inwards, or start from the inner ring and read outwards to the edge (so they are all five-letter words). Solutions to Circular clues read in either a clockwise or an anti-clockwise direction round the circle.

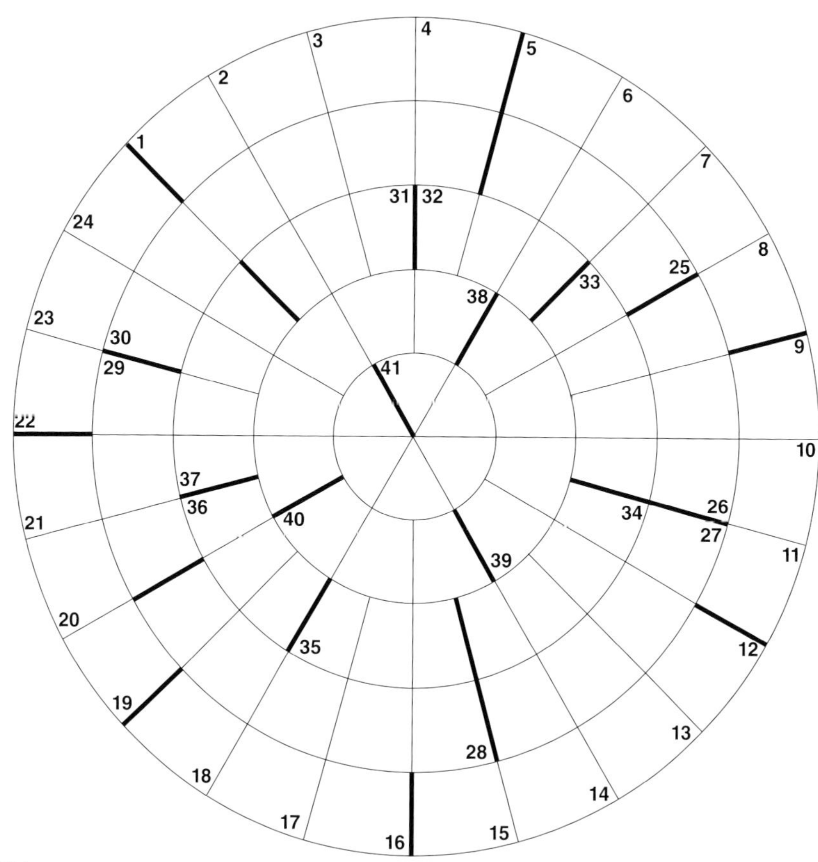

RADIAL: INWARDS

1 Tier
3 Black-and-white animal
6 Symbol
7 Wan
8 Grim-faced
9 Acquire knowledge
14 Drive away
15 Artist's stand
16 Spring month
18 Ointment
19 Animated
20 Black playing-card
21 Crowd
23 Proposal

OUTWARDS

2 Fragrance
4 Residence
5 Lessen
10 Small tropical fish
11 Enthusiasm
12 Murk
13 Dazzling light
17 Hobbles
22 Kingdom
24 Old style

CIRCULAR: CLOCKWISE

1 Lounge around
12 Lake
16 Beast of burden
19 Fire residue
22 Cow's low
27 Ripped
28 Horrify
30 Falsely charged when innocent
32 Acorn tree
33 Pile
34 Cleansing bar
37 Log boat
41 Fisherman

ANTI-CLOCKWISE

8 Gratify fully
11 Olive ___, Popeye's girlfriend
25 Drunkard
26 Domestic animal
29 Cut off branches
31 Lad
35 Married woman's title
36 Feel unwell
38 Produce offspring
39 Bait
40 Compete

Logic Problem

The conversation over a pot of tea between three women from a block of flats turned, as it often did, to the quality of TV programmes. From the clues given below, can you work out the number of each woman's flat, their current dislike and what they lamented the lack of?

Clues

1 It was Rose who maintained that comedy programmes are not a patch on what they were years ago.

2 The resident of number 16 did not comment on the lack of wholesome plays.

3 The lady who lamented the dearth of pleasant music did not also complain of loud background music; Hilda, who made neither of these criticisms, has a lower numbered flat than the woman who is exasperated by the whooping and cackling of studio audiences.

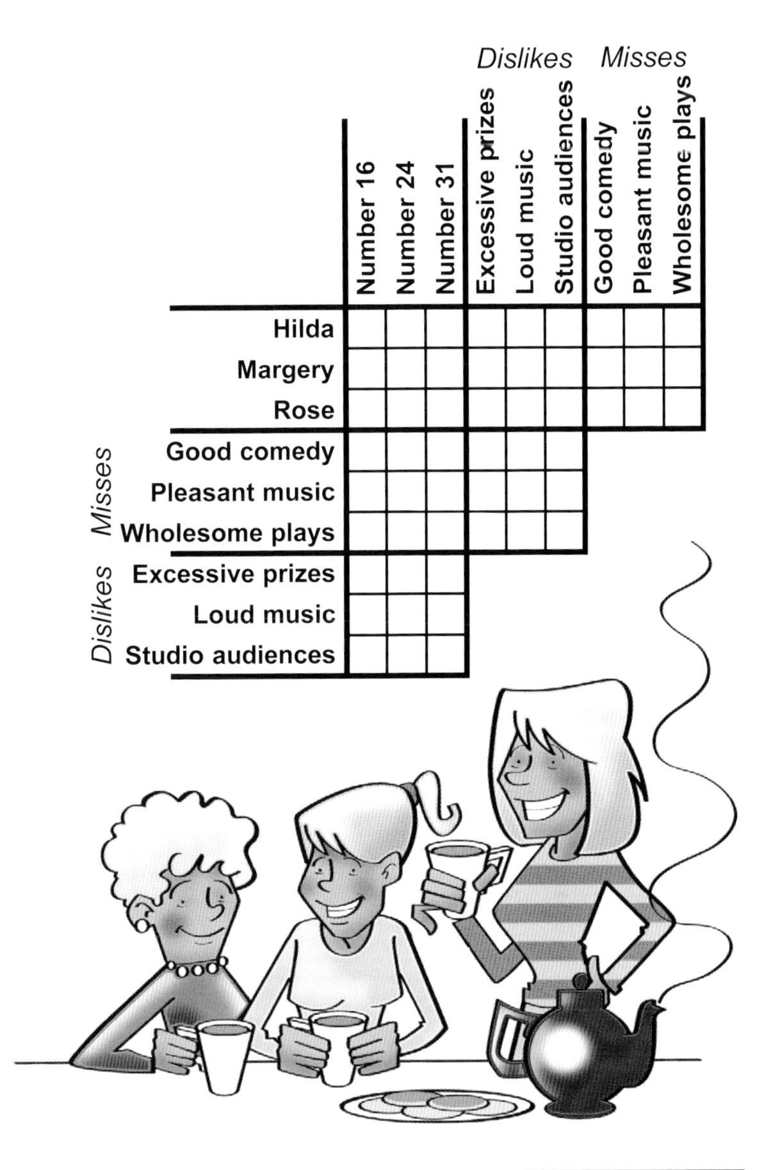

Woman	Flat	Dislike	Missed

Pathfinder

Beginning with the letter A in the shaded square, follow a single path to find 18 flowers. The trail passes through every letter once and may twist up, down and sideways (but never diagonally).

ANEMONE	IRIS
AZALEA	LILAC
BLUEBELL	LILY
CELANDINE	MAGNOLIA
CLEMATIS	ORCHID
DAFFODIL	PANSY
DAISY	PRIMROSE
DANDELION	SNOWDROP
HYACINTH	TULIP

D	N	A	D	A	L	I	P	L	A	C
E	T	I	S	Z	U	T	L	I	A	D
L	A	E	L	A	S	Y	N	A	F	F
I	M	A	D	A	I	Y	S	P	L	O
O	E	A	I	N	G	L	I	L	I	D
N	L	C	L	O	A	M	L	Y	C	H
I	R	I	S	H	B	L	L	O	R	I
W	O	N	S	T	N	U	E	R	P	D
D	H	Y	A	C	I	E	B	I	M	R
R	E	N	I	D	N	A	L	E	C	O
O	P	A	N	E	M	O	N	E	E	S

Solutions

Wordsearch

T	I	N	I	M	E	G	P	T	S	R	T	S	K	R	T	P	W	S	R	I
T	S	R	C	S	I	T	B	C	D	N	R	S	I	T	P	N	R	I	S	T
C	D	E	Y	H	H	A	Y	F	E	S	T	I	V	A	L	R	E	G	N	I
S	K	O	T	A	E	L	A	N	I	F	P	U	C	A	F	G	U	U	T	R
N	B	I	P	N	D	L	S	W	O	C	D	T	R	N	N	B	G	I	S	O
G	H	T	U	R	O	Y	S	N	I	S	E	O	C	I	D	R	O	T	P	N
I	E	G	B	S	N	C	A	E	O	R	E	D	L	T	M	H	N	N	U	L
I	G	E	N	E	E	C	G	M	A	D	S	L	A	A	K	O	I	R	O	D
T	I	O	A	E	E	N	F	N	L	F	O	S	Y	R	R	E	M	O	A	P
A	W	R	T	I	U	H	N	U	O	R	L	P	E	E	A	C	E	V	D	E
L	S	G	R	G	Q	A	M	O	E	S	O	O	N	B	E	P	I	I	T	T
N	A	E	R	E	Y	S	E	S	O	L	N	A	W	L	I	D	L	T	M	A
N	E	C	C	D	A	A	E	M	E	H	T	O	R	E	B	U	Y	P	A	A
S	S	L	E	O	M	E	I	L	E	L	A	T	I	E	R	G	K	N	I	Q
M	U	O	E	R	H	F	S	K	E	R	Y	O	C	S	I	S	A	B	A	U
E	R	O	C	C	D	N	T	B	L	A	A	K	R	H	I	E	H	S	U	A
A	U	N	I	O	N	T	E	P	D	R	H	L	W	A	L	V	G	O	S	R
I	A	E	M	E	O	C	D	E	N	A	R	T	D	A	E	I	O	S	W	I
H	T	Y	L	O	U	E	V	A	M	N	R	B	T	I	S	E	F	R	C	D
R	E	T	R	A	C	M	A	H	N	O	B	A	N	E	L	E	H	D	U	S
O	A	P	L	L	I	L	Y	O	F	T	H	E	V	A	L	L	E	Y	R	E

Suko

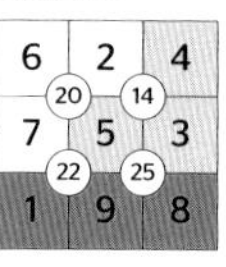

Wordsearch

E	D	M	S	F	I	R	E	H	P
U	Y	I	K	A	E	W	U	T	R
C	E	J	A	T	F	N	O	E	E
S	C	L	A	T	T	E	T	N	F
E	O	W	G	I	S	L	T	T	I
R	M	D	N	N	E	R	L	Y	N
D	P	G	O	H	U	H	I	C	K
O	A	R	S	A	L	J	A	F	G
O	S	L	A	V	I	V	R	U	S
F	S	I	N	S	E	C	T	M	O

Sudoku

8	9	7	2	3	4	6	1	5
3	4	5	1	9	6	7	2	8
1	2	6	5	8	7	4	3	9
6	5	1	7	2	8	9	4	3
9	8	3	4	5	1	2	7	6
2	7	4	9	6	3	5	8	1
5	3	8	6	4	2	1	9	7
4	1	9	3	7	5	8	6	2
7	6	2	8	1	9	3	5	4

Number Jig

	6		3	8	7		7	
1	5	8	0		2		2	
	2		7		7	3	4	3
3	6	6	3	3			6	
0		1			2	7	2	3
7	7	0	5		8		4	
2			5	7	2	7	6	1
0			8		7			4
9	3	2	4	1	3	6		1

Short Code

L	A	I	R	■	R	A	I	L
■	L	■	E	V	E	R	■	A
V	E	S	T	■	S	T	I	R
I	■	■	R	■	T	■	■	V
R	A	T	E	■	A	R	E	A
U	■	E	A	S	T	■	R	■
S	U	E	T	■	E	U	R	O

E	S	R	O	T
U	A	L	V	I

Noughts and Crosses

1	3	3	3	4	4	1
4	O	O	X	O	X	4
2	O	X	X	O	O	3
2	O	O	O	O	O	2
5	X	O	X	O	X	4
4	O	X	O	X	O	4
1	3	2	7	1	4	1

Linkword

COAL, CALM, POST, DOOR, PAGE, SOUL, SALT **OCTOPUS**

Sudoku

9	4	8	6	2	7	1	3	5
3	6	5	9	1	4	8	2	7
7	1	2	8	5	3	9	4	6
8	5	1	4	3	2	6	7	9
4	9	3	7	8	6	5	1	2
6	2	7	5	9	1	4	8	3
2	7	4	1	6	9	3	5	8
1	8	6	3	7	5	2	9	4
5	3	9	2	4	8	7	6	1

Brickwork

Add Up

68

Word Ladder

HORN, corn, core, coke, poke, pike, PIPE

Suguru

5	1	4	3	2	1	4
4	3	5	1	4	5	3
2	1	2	3	2	1	2
3	4	5	4	5	4	5
1	2	3	1	3	1	2
3	4	5	2	5	4	3
1	2	3	4	1	2	1

Arroword

Roger Bannister

Kids' Corner

1 Stockholm Sweden, 2 Cape Town South Africa, 3 New Delhi India

Honeycomb

1 Remark 2 Embark 3 Hybrid
4 Madrid 5 Baking 6 Tiring
7 Ablaze 8 Breeze 9 Drawer
10 Killer 11 Ripest 12 Honest
13 Lolita 14 Endure 15 Andrew
16 Lethal 17 Petite 18 Novice
19 Titles 20 Rupees 21 Ermine
22 Aherne 23 Tigger 24 Cinder
25 Thrill 26 Palace 27 Malawi
28 Easier 29 Gasbag 30 Nagged
31 Litter 32 Canter 33 Warder
34 Either 35 Abbess 36 Egress
37 Truest 38 Newest 39 Reward
40 Trough 41 Brogue 42 Remake
43 Septet 44 Secret 45 Rabies
46 Guides 47 Uglier 48 Kaiser
49 Crowds 50 Bipeds 51 Idling
52 Living 53 Pearly 54 Likely.

Two for Tea

Four Square

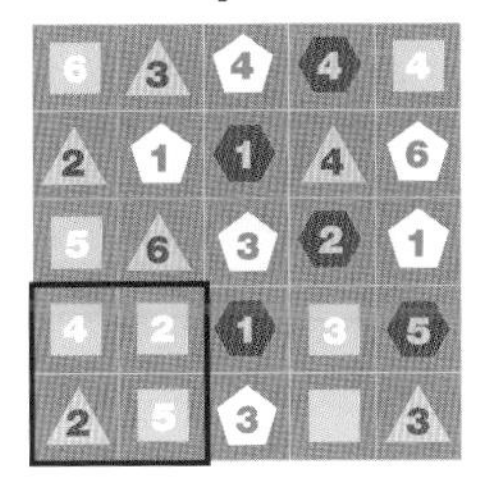

Jumbo Codeword

Amy Johnson

Roundabout

RADIAL: 1 Layer 2 Aroma 3 Zebra 4 Abode 5 Abate 6 Token 7 Ashen 8 Stern 9 Learn 10 Guppy 11 Gusto 12 Gloom 13 Glare 14 Repel 15 Easel 16 April 17 Limps 18 Salve 19 Alive 20 Spade 21 Horde 22 Realm 23 Offer 24 Retro.
CIRCULAR: 1 Laze 8 Sate 11 Oyl 12 Mere 16 Ass 19 Ash 22 Moo 25 Sot 26 Pet 27 Tore 28 Appal 29 Lop 30 Framed 31 Boy 32 Oak 33 Heap 34 Soap 35 Mrs 36 Ail 37 Raft 38 Breed 39 Lure 40 Vie 41 Angler.

Logic Problem

The woman who lamented the dearth of pleasant music was not Rose, whose complaint was about the decline of comedy programmes (clue 1), or Hilda (clue 3), so must have been Margery. Therefore Hilda's grievance must have been the lack of wholesome plays. So her flat is not number 16 (clue 2) and cannot be 31 (clue 3), so must be 24. She did not criticise the music or the behaviour of studio audiences (clue 3), so must resent the excessive prize money. It must therefore be the resident of number 31 who is irritated by studio audiences and the one from number 16 who objects to the loud music (clue 3). She cannot be Margery (clue 3), so must be Rose, leaving Margery with flat 31.
In summary: Hilda, number 24, excessive prize money, wholesome plays. Margery, number 31, studio audiences, pleasant music. Rose, number 16, loud music, good comedy.

Pathfinder

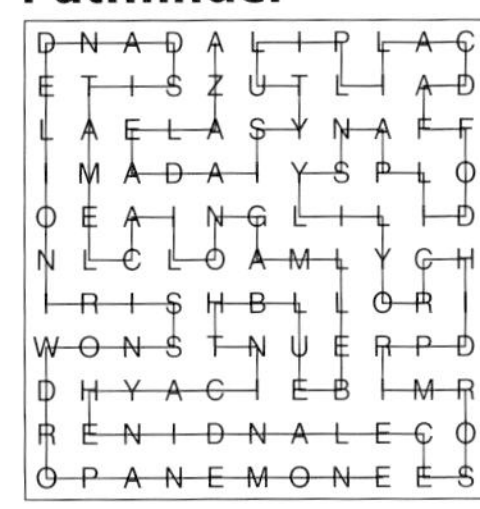

June

"I know this goes without saying, but Stonehenge really was the most incredible accomplishment. It took five hundred men just to pull each sarsen, plus a hundred more to dash around positioning the rollers. Just think about it for a minute. Can you imagine trying to talk six hundred people into helping you drag a fifty-ton stone eighteen miles across the countryside and muscle it into an upright position, and then saying, 'Right, lads! Another twenty like that, plus some lintels and maybe a couple of dozen nice bluestones from Wales, and we can party!' Whoever was the person behind Stonehenge was one dickens of a motivator, I'll tell you that."

Bill Bryson, Notes from a Small Island

Wordsearch

Find all the listed words associated with weddings.

- BEST MAN
- BUTTONHOLE
- CELEBRATE
- CEREMONY
- CHURCH
- CIVIL PARTNERSHIP
- CONFETTI
- COUPLE
- DRESS
- FIRST KISS
- GIVE AWAY
- GROOM
- GUEST
- HAPPINESS
- HONEYMOON
- HORSE AND CARRIAGE
- HUSBAND
- HYMN
- I DO
- I WILL
- KISS THE BRIDE
- LIMOUSINE
- LOVE
- MARRY
- NUPTIALS
- ORGAN
- PEW
- PHOTOGRAPH
- PRESENT
- PROMISE
- RECEPTION
- RICE
- RINGS
- ROMANCE
- ROSES
- SERMON
- SERVICE
- SIGN THE REGISTER
- SUIT
- TIE THE KNOT
- TOP HAT
- TOSS THE BOUQUET
- TRADITION
- TRAIN
- VEIL
- VICAR
- VIDEO
- VOWS
- WEDDING MARCH
- WIFE

MONDAY
1

TUESDAY
2

WEDNESDAY
3

THURSDAY
4

FRIDAY
5

SATURDAY
6

SUNDAY
7

MONDAY
8

Suko

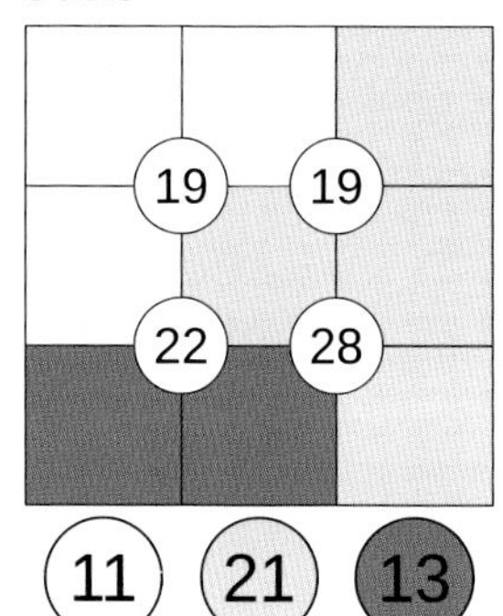

Wordsearch

W	G	O	N	D	O	L	A	D	E
A	Y	T	T	H	C	A	Y	H	O
R	Y	R	U	R	F	E	I	O	N
S	H	S	R	G	E	F	T	W	A
H	G	E	R	E	P	P	I	L	C
I	N	I	B	E	F	L	N	K	S
P	I	T	D	A	L	E	P	I	S
E	D	A	N	U	R	U	S	O	T
E	L	C	C	R	N	G	A	R	K
O	A	S	I	T	N	S	E	E	O

ARK
BARGE
CANOE
CLIPPER
DHOW
DINGHY
FERRY
GONDOLA
PEDALO
PUNT
SCULL
SKIFF
TUG
WARSHIP
YACHT

Sudoku

		5						
8	9	2	7			6		
		4	5				2	
				7				
9	7			3	5			
	2		8			3	5	
1	4					2	8	9
5		6	2	9			4	
	3	9		8			1	

TUESDAY
9

WEDNESDAY
10

THURSDAY
11

FRIDAY
12

SATURDAY
13

SUNDAY
14

MONDAY
15

TUESDAY
16

Number Jig

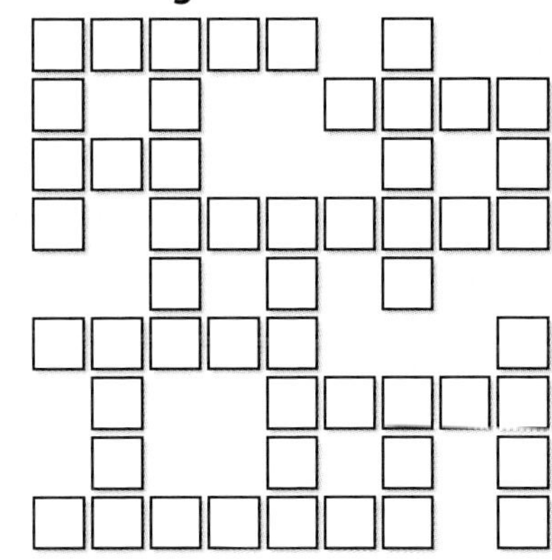

3 digits
538
962
971

4 digits
1853
3289
6260
9650

5 digits
62671
72988
76135
96467

6 digits
375706
448961

7 digits
4043611
9031782

Short Code

The Great Divide

Divide up the grid into four equally sized, equally shaped parts, each containing five different coloured balls.

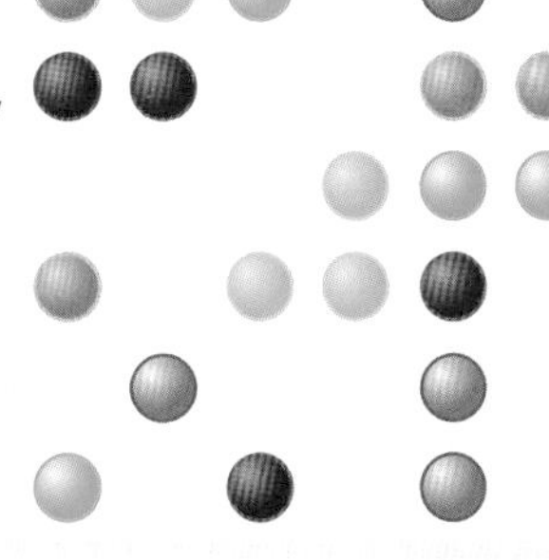

WEDNESDAY
17

THURSDAY
18

FRIDAY
19

SATURDAY
20

SUNDAY *FATHER'S DAY*
21

MONDAY
22

TUESDAY
23

WEDNESDAY
24

Linkword

WELL					CLEAR
BEAN					CHEESE
WATER					COURSE
SILICON					PAN
COMBINATION					OUT
LIVE					BRUSH
BEER					PEG

Sudoku

8		9					2	
					9			1
2		7	1	8		9	3	
		4	7		5		9	3
		3		1				
	6		4					
		1						7
7		8	6					
	5		9			4		

Brickwork

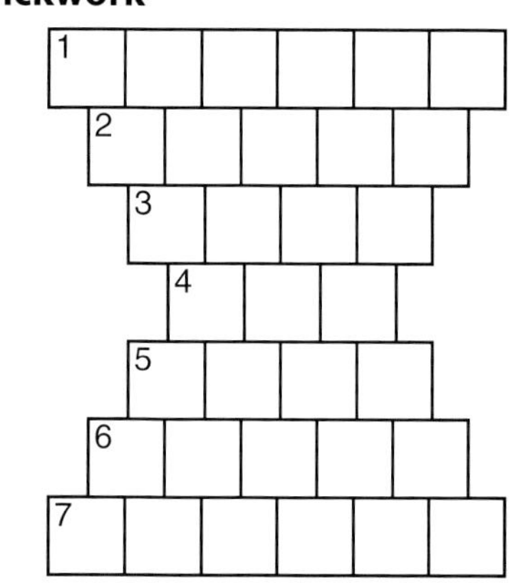

1 Main element found in coal (6)
2 Dangerous snake (5)
3 Wild pig (4)
4 Underwear item (3)
5 Dowdy, lacklustre (4)
6 Bakery product (5)
7 Lilo (3,3)

THURSDAY
25

FRIDAY
26

SATURDAY
27

SUNDAY
28

MONDAY
29

TUESDAY
30

NOTES

Add Up

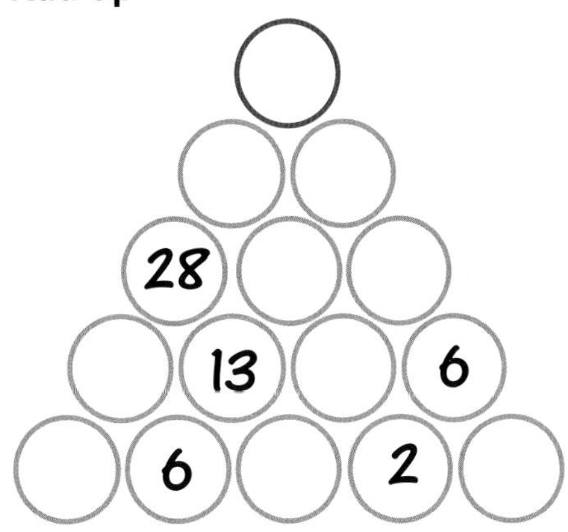

Word Ladder

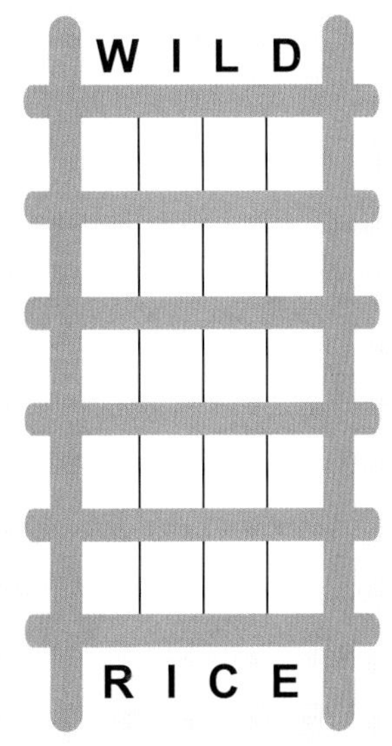

Suguru

		1			5	
		4	3			
			5			
4					2	
	4					

Crossword

The letters in the shaded squares spell out the name of a famous battle which took place in June 1815.

ACROSS

1 Lout (4)
6 Imitate (4)
8 Duplicate (7)
9 Which person? (3)
11 Bend in the middle (3)
13 Red-nosed joker (5)
16 Source of mutton (5)
18 Common, typical (5)
19 Old-fashioned (5)
20 Tear-making vegetable (5)
21 Correct in all details (5)
22 ___ Fitzgerald, jazz great (4)
25 As well (4)
27 Twinge (of hunger) (4)
28 Put goods into (a van) (4)
29 Newborn child (4)
31 ___ Coward, *Hay Fever* playwright (4)
34 Fizzy beer served cold (5)
37 Cowboy's looped rope (5)
38 Butcher's scraps (5)
39 Hollow tube used for drinking (5)
40 Less good (5)
43 Liquid discharged by an aerosol (5)
46 Grief, sorrow (3)
49 Slippery as an ___, fishy saying (3)
50 Variety of crossword clue (7)
51 Make (woollens) (4)
52 Door lockers (4)

DOWN

2 Cry of a wolf (4)
3 Become larger (4)
4 ___ for, select (3)
5 Auction offer (3)
6 Notes and coins (4)
7 Part of a book (4)
10 Cheap lodgings for travellers (6)
12 Television and radio signal receiver (6)
13 Borrow, sponge (5)
14 Painting of an unclothed figure (4)
15 Large wild American cat (4)
16 Narrow hole for coins (4)
17 Seasonal children's play (5)
23 South American woolly pack animal (5)
24 Furious (5)
25 Woody ___, actor/ director (see picture) (5)
26 Emptiness between galaxies (5)
29 Local rule (5)
30 French-style cafe (6)
32 In flames (2,4)
33 Sweet on a stick (5)
34 Opposite of 'win' (4)
35 Involving bloodshed (4)
36 Lines (of seats) (4)
41 ___ Glendower, Welsh hero (4)
42 Religious group (4)
44 Hasty kiss (4)
45 Country on your side (4)
47 Cheerio (3)
48 And so forth (abbrev)(3)

Jigword

3 letters
BUY
CEP
CUR
HUT
PUG
TOM
WAD
YEW

4 letters
ACRE
ISLE
NOOK
RIDE
~~ROSE~~
SETT
TWIT
VEIN

5 letters
BAIZE
DEIGN
ETHER
GRAVE
LEMUR
MERGE
MUMMY
RATIO
SPUME
UTTER

6 letters
CAVITY
IREFUL
LAWYER
LITMUS
METRIC
OCELOT
UNEASE
WALNUT

7 letters
EXHAUST
EYEBROW
FLIGHTY
FREEZER
GENTEEL
GYMNAST
MARQUEE
OBLIQUE
OMNIBUS
RISIBLE
STERILE
ULULATE
UNITARY

8 letters
CELLULAR
ENVISAGE
LACERATE
REMEDIAL
STUBBORN

9 letters
ADULATION
BAKEHOUSE
BUBBLEGUM
UNHEALTHY
VOLUNTEER

10 letters
WILLOWHERB

11 letters
BOILERMAKER
POLLINATION
TOXOPHILITE

Magic Square

Complete the Magic Square so that it contains nine consecutive numbers, and all rows, columns and diagonals add up to the same total.

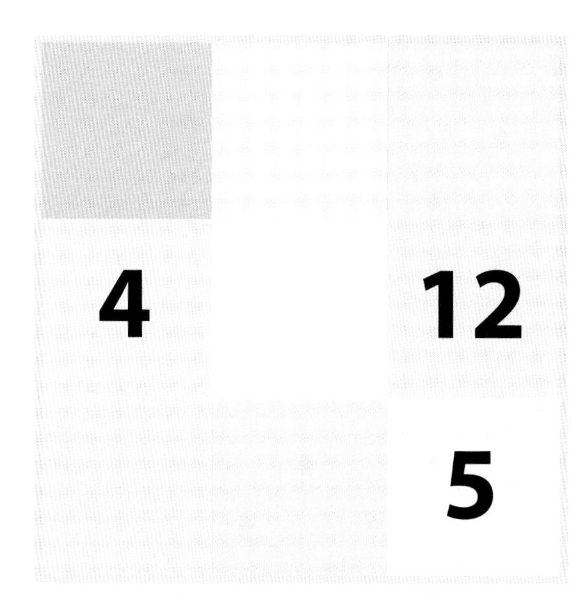

Two Timer

Two sets of clues to the same answers.

STRAIGHT CLUES

ACROSS

1 Old gold or silver coin (5)
4 Venomous snake of the British Isles (5)
7 Take place (5)
9 Organ that removes toxins from the blood (5)
10 Full of substance (5)
11 Pertinent, relevant (3)
13 Top records chart (3,6)
16 News or data (11)
17 Person who is not keeping up with a group (9)
19 Vigour, vim (3)
21 Code word between hotel and Juliet (5)
23 Declare to be void (5)
24 Shout of praise or encouragement (5)
25 Foremost in time, order, or importance (5)
26 Containing nothing, vacant (5)

DOWN

1 Triangular tract of land at a river's mouth (5)
2 Jealously desire (5)
3 Sad anthem of lost or unrequited love (5,4)
4 Prepare for war (3)
5 Art of writing and presenting plays (5)
6 Correspondence in word sounds (5)
8 Look thoughtfully at (11)
12 Division on a compass (5)
14 Post-operative treatment (9)
15 Movement to music (5)
17 Lacking ease of movement (5)
18 Tracking device using electromagnetic waves (5)
19 Celebrity wall-poster (3-2)
20 Chummy (5)
22 Law passed by Parliament (3)

CRYPTIC CLUES

ACROSS

1 Coin one found in channel (5)
4 Slipper with zigzag pattern (5)
7 Happen to find old dog about to be included (5)
9 One existing organ (5)
10 Beefy perhaps and full of interest (5)
11 New tap fitting (3)
13 Pirate had organised list of most popular things (3,6)
16 Knowledge systematically arranged (11)
17 Last person to go irregularly on right (9)
19 Go both ways (3)
21 Endlessly aiding rebuilding country (5)
23 Ban, nullify part or abolish (5)
24 Comfort companion at all times (5)
25 Earliest academic degree (5)
26 In contempt you left it unfurnished (5)

DOWN

1 Greek character in alluvial area (5)
2 Envy company doctor (5)
3 Light music? (5,4)
4 Some harmful weapon (3)
5 What RADA members performed Frenchman included (5)
6 It is soundly similar at the end (5)
8 Intend to study pattern (11)
12 Sharp position in the field? (5)
14 Medical aid following race disaster (9)
15 Square ball? (5)
17 Body not easily bent (5)
18 Method of detection going up and down just the same (5)
19 Picture inside young dog going round (3-2)
20 Play quietly with friend who is friendly (5)
22 One of a number of things done in the New Testament (3)

Quiz Wordsearch

Answer the given clues and then find the answers hidden in the grid.

1 Annual European cycle race (4,2,6)

2 Australian actress whose birthday is 20th June (6,6)

3 British tennis Grand Slam tournament (9)

4 Dot in *EastEnders* (4,5)

5 Famous pop festival (11)

6 Horse race at Epsom (3,5)

7 Lara Croft actress whose birthday is 4th June (8,5)

8 Line of latitude the Sun reaches in June (6,2,6)

9 One of the Beatles whose birthday is 18th June (4,9)

10 *Purple Rain* singer whose birthday is 7th June (6)

11 Rodgers and Hammerstein musical featuring the song 'June is busting out all over' (8)

12 Sovereign's Official Birthday ceremony (8,3,6)

13 *Sweeney Todd* actor whose birthday is 9th June (6,4)

14 Veteran actress in Ab Fab (4,9)

15 Wife of Johnny Cash (4,6)

Logic Problem

While the Neolithic residents of Wiltshire travelled to their slightly ostentatious circle of stones on Midsummer's Day, our five cave-dwelling friends, who live too far away to make the journey, have to make do with their own miniature versions of the henge. From the clues, can you say from what each man has made his circle, at what time of day he performs the sun-worshipping ritual and to what purpose he puts his micro-henge for the rest of the year?

Clues

1. Igg performed his Midsummer's Day ritual later than the man who built his mini-henge from rocks gathered from the riverbank, but earlier than the man whose hengelet is used to predict migration of the game herds; the latter construction isn't the bite-sized-henge made from antlers that is worshipped at in the middle of the morning.
2. Ogg has made his baby henge from axe heads blunted beyond repair; he doesn't observe Midsummer's Day at dusk.
3. When it's not midsummer Ugg uses his milli-henge to calculate when a fishing trip would be profitable; the log henge is used as a weather forecasting device, but isn't the site of the dawn worship on Midsummer's Day.
4. Egg performs his worship when the sun is at its highest in the sky, although it'll be a millennium or two before it's called 'noon'.
5. The man who uses his itsy-henge to help heal wounds celebrates later than Agg.

	Antlers	Axe heads	Bones	Logs	Rocks	Dawn	Mid morning	Noon	Mid afternoon	Dusk	Fishing predictor	Healing wounds	Migration predictor	Summon spirits	Weather forecast
Agg															
Egg															
Igg															
Ogg															
Ugg															
Fishing predictor															
Healing wounds															
Migration predictor															
Summon spirits															
Weather forecast															
Dawn															
Mid morning															
Noon															
Mid afternoon															
Dusk															

Caveman	Henge material	Time of day	Other use

Jolly Mixtures

ACROSS
1 POOR RATE
6 BUTS
8 COAT
9 COASTING
10 FELT
11 GENERA
13 LEAR
15 RADON
17 MATED
19 NEMO
21 ANTLER
24 GOER
26 LAYERING
27 ORLA
28 TEST
29 DREAD KEN

DOWN
2 HEAPS
3 SO RETRO
4 RETARD
5 ANGER
6 SABRE
7 ENGLISH
12 ETON
14 ANNO
16 STEEPED
18 MEAN ONE
20 GERMAN
22 CARET
23 TIRED
25 LAGER

1	2		3		4		5	■	6		7	
■		■		■		■		■		■		■
8				■	9							
■		■		■		■		■		■		■
10				■		■	11	12				
■	■	■	13	14			■		■	■		■
15	16				■	■	■	17	18			
■		■	■		■	19	20			■	■	■
21			22		23	■		■	24		25	
■		■		■		■		■		■		■
26								■	27			
■		■		■		■		■		■		■
28				■	29							

Solutions

Wordsearch

P	C	H	S	S	E	R	D	Y	Q	T	O	F	L	L	S	P	S	F	L	A
R	L	E	C	H	U	R	C	H	A	E	O	S	S	E	N	I	P	P	A	H
E	V	O	L	R	A	K	A	L	D	W	D	P	R	M	G	H	F	A	H	B
S	L	A	Y	E	A	D	A	I	L	V	A	V	H	N	A	S	A	O	B	E
E	S	H	L	A	B	M	V	R	I	T	I	E	T	A	D	R	N	K	N	S
N	S	I	O	A	N	R	G	C	O	C	F	H	V	L	T	E	R	O	G	T
T	L	E	K	R	A	N	A	N	E	M	E	Y	U	I	Y	N	I	Y	R	M
T	A	E	D	T	S	R	K	T	I	R	A	I	L	M	G	T	A	B	O	A
O	I	O	D	I	S	E	T	E	E	D	T	N	O	N	P	R	P	A	O	N
S	T	U	E	L	H	R	A	G	N	T	D	O	C	E	E	A	H	C	M	D
S	P	A	S	T	A	L	I	N	E	U	N	E	C	E	E	P	O	L	A	G
T	U	N	E	I	L	S	E	F	D	F	S	E	W	K	Y	L	T	A	B	N
H	N	I	N	I	T	E	N	C	D	C	R	E	N	L	R	I	O	E	U	O
E	T	A	W	E	N	O	T	E	D	N	A	B	S	U	H	V	G	R	A	I
B	E	I	R	L	C	E	L	P	U	O	C	R	V	O	G	I	R	S	S	T
O	S	P	B	U	T	T	O	N	H	O	L	E	R	N	R	C	A	G	I	I
U	I	M	E	E	C	D	O	M	N	R	I	T	A	I	A	E	P	N	V	D
Q	M	I	S	W	L	M	O	Y	U	L	W	E	A	N	A	G	H	I	O	A
U	O	E	D	I	R	B	E	H	T	S	S	I	K	R	B	G	R	R	W	R
E	R	G	U	E	S	T	T	Y	I	S	E	F	F	R	I	C	E	O	S	T
T	P	C	S	L	I	M	O	U	S	I	N	E	C	E	R	E	M	O	N	Y

Number Jig

9	6	4	6	7		6		
6		4			3	2	8	9
5	3	8				6		6
0		9	0	3	1	7	8	2
		6		7		1		
7	6	1	3	5				1
	2			7	2	9	8	8
	6			0		7		5
4	0	4	3	6	1	1		3

Linkword

KEPT, CURD, MAIN, CHIP, LOCK, WIRE, TENT **PUMPKIN**

Sudoku

8	1	9	3	5	7	6	2	4
6	3	5	2	4	9	8	7	1
2	4	7	1	8	6	9	3	5
1	8	4	7	6	5	2	9	3
9	7	3	8	1	2	5	4	6
5	6	2	4	9	3	7	1	8
4	9	1	5	2	8	3	6	7
7	2	8	6	3	4	1	5	9
3	5	6	9	7	1	4	8	2

Short Code

E	L	T	Y	N
V	O	S	A	I

Brickwork

CARBON
COBRA
BOAR
BRA
DRAB
BREAD
AIRBED

Add Up

87

Suko

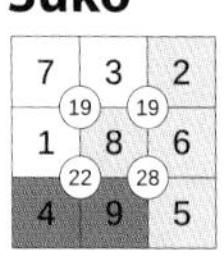

Wordsearch

W	G	O	N	D	O	L	A	D	E
A	Y	T	T	H	C	A	Y	H	O
R	Y	R	U	B	F	E	I	O	N
S	H	S	R	G	E	F	T	W	A
H	G	E	R	E	P	P	I	L	C
I	N	I	B	E	F	L	N	K	S
P	I	T	D	A	L	E	P	I	S
E	D	A	N	U	R	U	S	O	T
E	L	C	C	R	N	G	A	R	K
O	A	S	I	T	N	S	E	E	O

The Great Divide

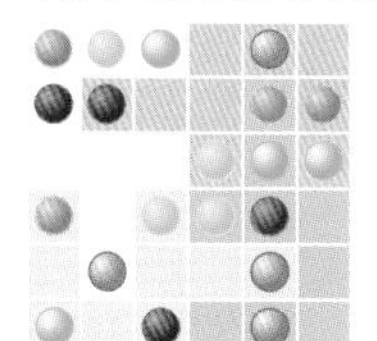

Word Ladder

WILD, mild, mile, male, mace, race, RICE

Sudoku

3	6	5	9	2	8	1	7	4
8	9	2	7	1	4	6	3	5
7	1	4	5	6	3	9	2	8
4	5	3	6	7	2	8	9	1
9	7	8	1	3	5	4	6	2
6	2	1	8	4	9	3	5	7
1	4	7	3	5	6	2	8	9
5	8	6	2	9	1	7	4	3
2	3	9	4	8	7	5	1	6

Suguru

1	2	1	2	1	5	1
3	5	4	3	4	3	4
2	1	2	1	2	5	1
3	5	4	5	3	4	3
4	2	3	2	1	2	1
1	5	1	4	3	4	3
2	4	3	2	1	2	1

Solutions

Crossword

Waterloo

Quiz Wordsearch

```
A K T Y S L E S U O R A C S S S S S A M A
N S I R R H A S T E C N A R F E D R U O T
G I A G O U M S K J T I A H D L S A P I D
E T E A R P B S U E I L T G M F A A N E L
L T R O O P I N G T H E C O L O U R A D E
I R H S I T E C O E A L N R E L I P M S I
N O A T Y B E W O T D L R G M N P J D M F
A I S A U K H Y I F S E O C T E R U I N T
J E F G A R R I L M C A C P D S W N K O I
O E C D T R R F A N B A L Y I E S E E L H
L J U N E C A R T E R L N G O G M B L H W
I T A D I R E N I T S N E C Y E O R O D E
E A E L R R T P N N H I E D E A S O C B N
O H R E T H P E U O L I G N O R M W I A U
T E C D S K Y O J R P I A E N N F N N L J
```

1 TOUR DE FRANCE
2 NICOLE KIDMAN
3 WIMBLEDON
4 JUNE BROWN
5 GLASTONBURY
6 THE DERBY
7 ANGELINA JOLIE
8 TROPIC OF CANCER
9 PAUL MCCARTNEY
10 PRINCE
11 CAROUSEL
12 TROOPING THE COLOUR
13 JOHNNY DEPP
14 JUNE WHITFIELD
15 JUNE CARTER

Jigword

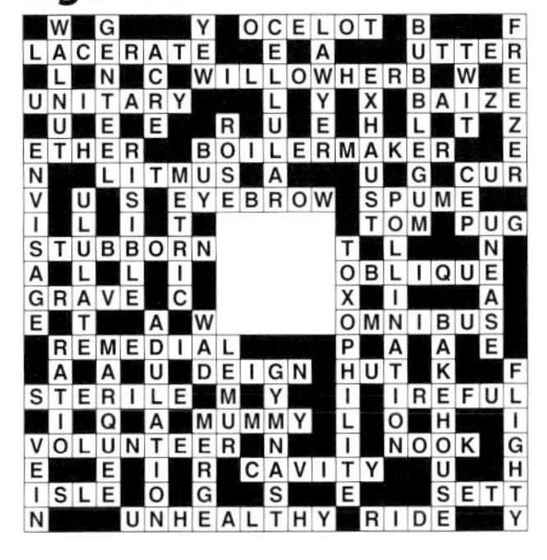

Magic Square

10	3	8
5	7	9
6	11	4

11	6	7
4	8	12
9	10	5

Two Timer

ACROSS: 1 Ducat 4 Adder 7 Occur 9 Liver 10 Meaty 11 Apt 13 Hit parade 16 Information 17 Straggler 19 Pep 21 India 23 Annul 24 Cheer 25 First 26 Empty.

DOWN: 1 Delta 2 Covet 3 Torch song 4 Arm 5 Drama 6 Rhyme 8 Contemplate 12 Point 14 Aftercare 15 Dance 17 Stiff 18 Radar 19 Pin-up 20 Pally 22 Act.

Logic Problem

Egg worships at noon (clue 4), so the dusk worshipper, who isn't Igg (clue 1), Ogg (clue 2) or Agg (clue 5) must be Ugg, who uses his henge as a fishing predictor (clue 3). The log henge was used as a weather forecaster (clue 3) and the antler henge was worshipped at in the middle of the morning (clue 4), so the fishing predicting henge worshipped at dusk which isn't made from rocks (clue 1) or axe heads (clue 2), must have been made from bones. The migration predicting henge isn't made from rocks or antlers (clue 1) and the log henge predicts the weather (clue 3), so the game migration predictor must be Ogg's axe-head henge (clue 2). We know it's not used for midsummer worship at mid morning, noon or dusk. Nor was it worshipped at dawn (clue 1), so it must have been paid homage to in the mid afternoon. Igg wasn't the dawn worshipper (clue 1), so he must have been the mid morning man with the antler henge, leaving Agg as the dawn worshipper. He doesn't own the log henge (clue 3) and must own the rock henge, leaving the weather forecasting log henge as the property of noon-worshipping Egg. Finally Agg doesn't use his rock henge to heal wounds so he must hope to summon the spirits of his ancestors with it, leaving Igg as the man whose antler henge is usually used to heal wounds.

Agg, rocks, dawn, summon spirits.

Egg, logs, noon, weather forecast.

Igg, antlers, mid morning, healing wounds.

Ogg, axe heads, mid afternoon, migration predictor.

Ugg, bones, dusk, fishing predictor.

Jolly Mixtures

July

Saint Swithin's Day 15 July:

St Swithin's day if thou dost rain
For forty days it will remain
St Swithin's day if thou be fair
For forty days 'twill rain nae mare

British weather lore proverb

Wordsearch

R F X Q O O F O C K O E E C O T E E O T G
M U F E C N H O L A R K S P U R T E N R E
S O B A T S D I R A U Q A A T L E D E C R
G N M Y S A K H E G O T H N E A P S O E C
T R F A N I E S N L O G M H T A R E N I S
X E B E N E D I C T C U M B E R B A T C H
O I C D A L L R N O O M E U L B I T P N B
R I R E J W A S O R E T H A U N S L S I R
G O N P O U M A E C D S T K D O Y R T T I
Y I B R D A L E N F L T S E R E A O S P T
A A K I T N I I H N A U P E C D D L W S I
D J G R N G A A U G M E O E I W I T I N S
E A R N E W S R E S N O L I W T L N T E H
L C D A I H I R G D C R U A P S O E H O O
L I L A T P Y L E H G A T N M E H R I F P
I S K O I E P N L Y S E E A E C R D N N E
T T L R L H C U E I R I S S U A E I S O N
S N T N E E P R N L A A T L A G M S D I G
A M E E D O C D I A N M R I T R M A A E O
B H I A S H L L O U W E S A R N U R Y B L
T Y Y I S E Y F C D O S A P L B S R G N F

Find all the listed words and phrases associated with July, together with stars celebrating their birthdays this month, hidden in the grid.

BASTILLE DAY
BENEDICT CUMBERBATCH
BLUE MOON
BRITISH GRAND PRIX
BRITISH OPEN GOLF
DELTA AQUARIDS
HENLEY REGATTA
INDEPENDENCE DAY
JK ROWLING
JULIUS CAESAR
LARKSPUR
ROBIN WILLIAMS
RUBY
ST SWITHIN'S DAY
SUMMER HOLIDAYS
SWAN UPPING
WATER LILY

WEDNESDAY
1

THURSDAY
2

FRIDAY
3

SATURDAY *AMERICAN INDEPENDENCE DAY*
4

SUNDAY
5

MONDAY
6

TUESDAY
7

WEDNESDAY
8

Suko

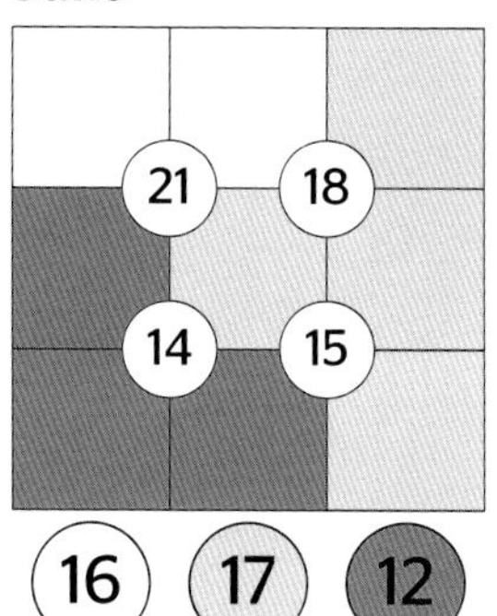

Wordsearch

S	L	P	P	A	S	J	E	X	T
G	E	L	A	E	D	A	I	B	T
G	C	L	I	N	D	O	U	A	G
E	O	R	F	N	C	R	S	C	O
L	F	I	U	F	G	A	N	O	D
E	F	S	T	E	A	R	K	N	T
K	E	R	R	I	L	W	I	E	O
A	E	E	I	N	W	O	R	B	H
H	N	H	T	O	O	B	T	P	S
S	C	J	U	K	E	B	O	X	D

BACON	EGGS	RIBS
BOOTH	FRIES	SHAKE
BROWNIE	HOT DOG	SODA
BURGER	JUKEBOX	SUNDAE
COFFEE	PANCAKE	WAFFLE

Sudoku

			6	9			8	
1						2		
	3	8		1		4		7
	4	3	9		1			
6	7				8			9
	8	9	4		7			
	6	7		3		8		2
3						6		
			5	7			3	

THURSDAY
9

FRIDAY
10

SATURDAY
11

SUNDAY
12

MONDAY
13

TUESDAY
14

WEDNESDAY
15

THURSDAY
16

Number Jig

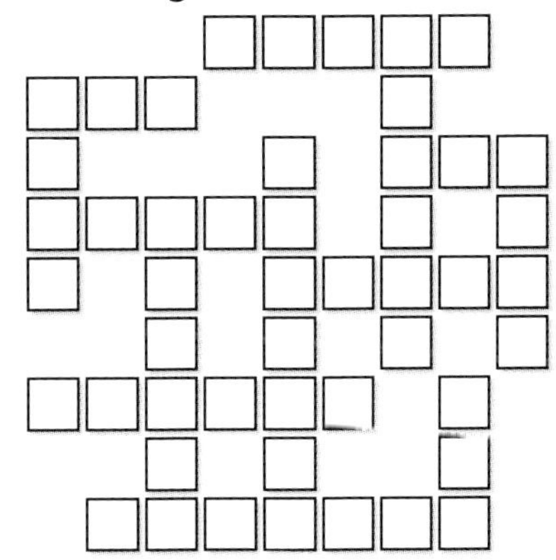

3 digits
230
644
759

4 digits
4651
7511

5 digits
10626
17724
61405

6 digits
226746
735037
930023

7 digits
4772270
6461262

Short Code

Dice Maze

Each colour represents a direction (up, down, left or right) and the number of dots on each dice tell you how far to go. Starting on the middle dice of the maze, follow the directions correctly and you will visit every dice in turn once only. Which dice is the last you visit on your trip?

Purple = Right; Green = Left; Blue = Up; Orange = Down.

FRIDAY
17

SATURDAY
18

SUNDAY
19

MONDAY
20

TUESDAY
21

WEDNESDAY
22

THURSDAY
23

FRIDAY
24

Linkword

STUDIO					CAP
FOLK					THRUSH
WEDDING					BINDER
SEE					GOES
BLIND					KICK
DIE					LABOUR
BUMPING					ORBIT

Sudoku

							6	
						9	5	1
8	1	9				3	2	
		1			4			
	5	8	3	2				
	4		9	5				
		4		1	7	8		
1			5	3		4		
	3					6		

Brickwork

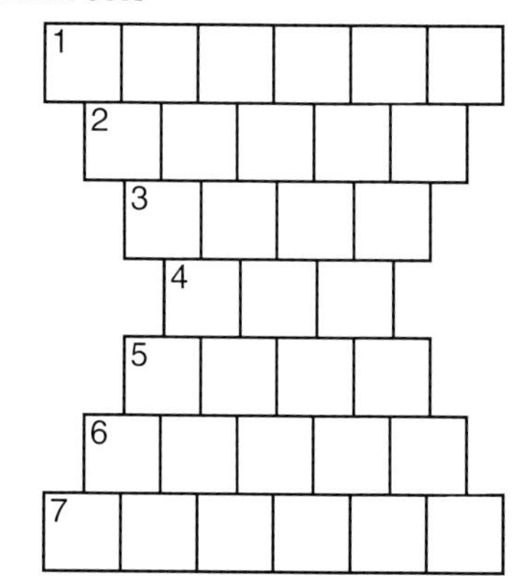

1 More quickly (6)
2 Later than (5)
3 Floating platform (4)
4 Long way off (3)
5 Wear at the edges (4)
6 _ story, imaginary tale (5)
7 Monks' home (6)

SATURDAY
25

SUNDAY
26

MONDAY
27

TUESDAY
28

WEDNESDAY
29

THURSDAY
30

FRIDAY
31

Add Up

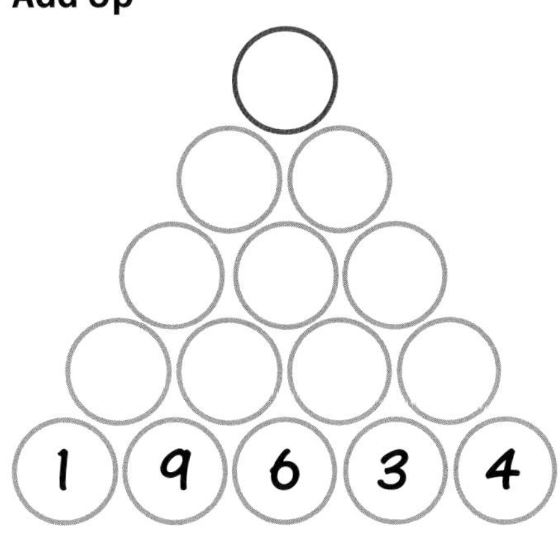

Word Ladder

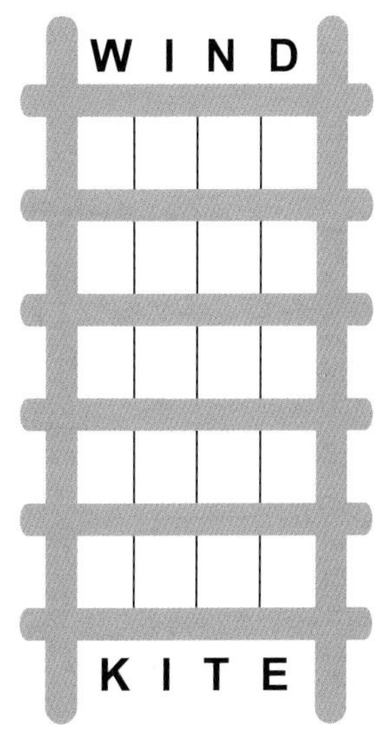

Suguru

					5	
3			5			
	4				3	4
2					4	
			2			
	4					

Arroword

Tiny jumping insect

Popular brew with a citrus flavour (5,3)

Rapid or rash

Middle of the body

Common plastic material

Split open

Thick string

Landing-stage for boats

__ Baba, pantomime character

Strong impulse

Sooty mark

Travel across snow

Robert De __, film star

First name of singer Mr Murs

Speak

Pimple

DecÕs partner

So far

Recently

Low number

Eyelid swelling

Place at an angle

Or __, otherwise

French or haricot, eg

Scotland, in Scottish Gaelic

Swiss mountain range

Game played on horseback

Beer

Person refusing to go on strike

Pointed nail on a bird's foot

Grip with the teeth

Part of your foot

__ lens, camera part

Performs in an exagger-ated way

Highest quantity

Spiny plants found in the desert

Fine delicate pottery

Owing money (2,4)

Lamb's mother

Game scored in runs (see picture)

__ Garai, actress

At what time?

Prison officers

Damaged by a blow

Border, rim

Particular sort

Let fall to the ground

Mentally healthy

Go mouldy

Get lost!

TeacherÕs favourite

First light of dawn

Slang name for a police officer

Unit of DNA

Go to the next page (inits)

Settle cosily

Verse writer

Relaxed in a chair

The letters in the shaded squares spell out the name of an event which took place in July 1985.

Kids' Corner

A-mazing

Poor Maisie has dug herself into a deep hole! Help her find her way through the sand tunnels to her ice cream.

Honeycomb

All the answers are six-letter words. Each answer is entered in a circle around its clue number. The first letter of the answer is entered in the shaded triangle immediately above the clue number. If the clue number is odd, enter the answer in an anti-clockwise direction. If the clue number is even, enter the answer in a clockwise direction.

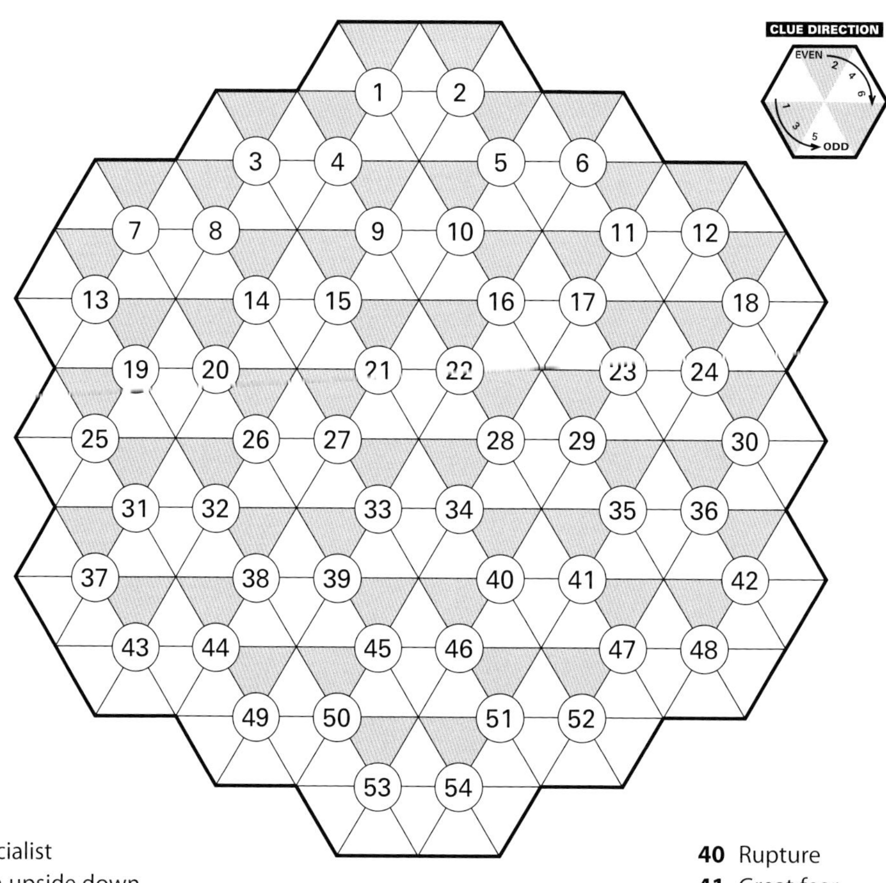

1 Specialist
2 Turn upside down
3 Prickly fish
4 Read carefully
5 Church robing-room
6 Recollection
7 Young child
8 Express agreement
9 Reddish-brown
10 Urban road
11 Unpretentious
12 Most sensible
13 Soft felt hat
14 Awkward predicament
15 Rubs hard
16 Entertain lavishly
17 University qualification
18 Blanket-like shawl
19 Provoked to anger
20 Separated
21 Writing desk
22 Four-wheeled carriage
23 Wayward
24 Obvious
25 Employee organisations
26 Not long past
27 Speak from memory
28 Ensnared
29 Eye membrane
30 Sequence of three cards
31 Head (colloq)
32 Settle snugly
33 Herbal infusion
34 Gas used as a fuel
35 Containing nitrogen
36 Fault-finder
37 Condemned
38 Fourteen-line verse
39 Musical composition
40 Rupture
41 Great fear
42 Collision
43 Colonial power
44 Bear with tolerance
45 Sampled
46 Without a doubt
47 Trying experience
48 Informal
49 Irish Republic capital
50 Stretch tightly
51 Formal discussion
52 Remove, erase
53 Pungent salad root
54 Expel from a country

Two for Tea

ACROSS
- **1** Number of legs on a tarantula (5)
- **4** Kentish hop kiln (4)
- **6** Electrical unit of resistance (3)
- **7** Royal period in office (5)
- **8** Hero, object of worship (4)
- **9** Of sailors and ships (5)
- **11** Underwater detection device (5)
- **13** Iconic small car (4)
- **14** More than adequately (5)
- **16** Animal covering (3)
- **17** French holiday home (4)
- **18** Inuit seal-skin canoe (5)

DOWN
- **1** Go wrong (3)
- **2** Bemoan, bewail (6)
- **3** Relating to musical key (5)
- **4** Overlook (4)
- **5** Opposite of 'shorter' (6)
- **9** Aromatic kernel (6)
- **10** Make it ___, hurry up! (6)
- **11** Ignite (5)
- **12** From birth to death (4)
- **15** Tibetan pack animal (3)

ACROSS
- **1** Abnormal fear (6)
- **6** Run after (5)
- **7** Specialist (6)
- **9** Three-legged seat (5)
- **12** Dangerous exploit (5)
- **14** Nation, country (5)
- **16** Tough cotton used for jeans (5)
- **19** Nearly (6)
- **21** Become ready to pick (5)
- **22** Annually (6)

DOWN
- **1** Push hard, squeeze or crush (5)
- **2** Elderly person (inits)(3)
- **3** Sections of a play (4)
- **4** Dessert similar to tapioca (4)
- **5** Touch (4)
- **8** Boredom (5)
- **10** ___ pole, Native American post (5)
- **11** Away from home (3)
- **13** Item of neckwear (3)
- **15** No ___, road sign (5)
- **16** Filth (4)
- **17** Back of the neck (4)
- **18** Lots (4)
- **20** Belonging to us (3)

Block Party

This used to be a big cube made of 216 small blocks measuring 6 by 6 by 6. If all the blocks that are not visible from this angle are present, can you work out how many have been taken away?

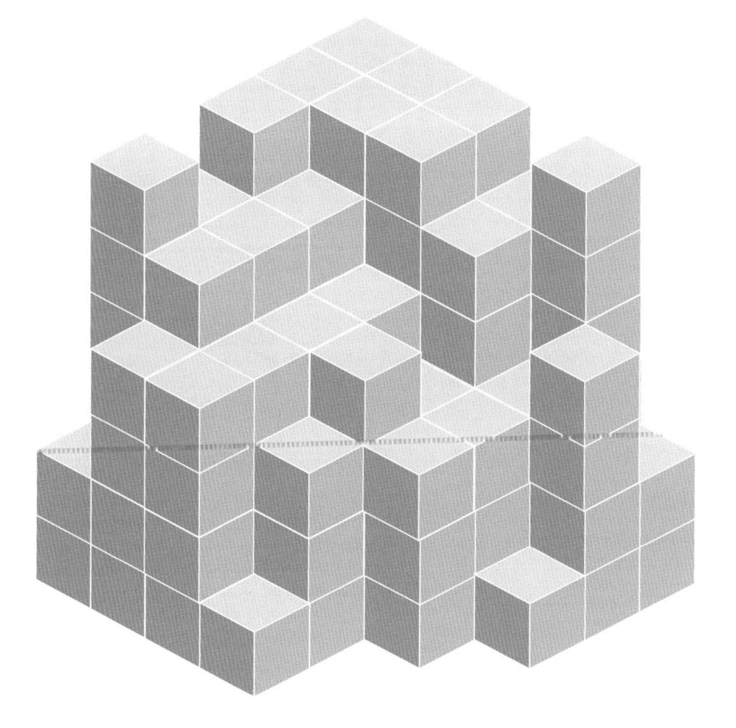

Spot the Difference

Can you spot the six differences between these two pictures?

Jumbo Codeword

The letters in the phrase box will spell out the name of a product which first arrived from Columbia in July 1586.

8 R	9 A	4 M	18	9	17	5	■	25	26	10	8	5
1	■	26	■	■	9	20	13	26	■	26	■	16
10	26	20	■	9	22	22	■	11	1	13	■	13
3	■	22	1	17	■	1	12	11	■	13	21	5
16	5	5	■	5	■	12	8	19	■	5	■	5
13	■	8	5	20	13	■	1	■	6	8	9	4
■	22	■	16	13	3	13	13	5	8	■	14	■
2	26	20	6	■	11	■	5	■	26	■	3	■
■	16	■	9	8	26	9	■	26	20	22	5	24
■	14	■	11	■	18	11	19	■	1	■	22	■
11	3	20	9	8	■	11	1	11	11	■	3	■
■	26	■	13	■	16	■	3	■	26	13	6	21
■	5	■	1	15	5	8	8	9	20	■	13	■
16	13	26	8	■	18	■	16	13	5	18	■	7
18	■	20	■	9	26	22	■	1	■	1	12	5
8	26	22	■	10	9	8	■	20	26	13	■	8
3	■	26	15	19	■	9	13	5	■	9	8	23
20	■	17	■	16	9	25	5	■	■	13	■	5
17	11	1	16	16	■	13	9	10	11	1	26	22

A B C D E F G H I J K L M N O P Q R S T U V W X Y Z

1	2	3	4	5	6	7	8	9	10	11	12	13
			M				R	A				
14	15	16	17	18	19	20	21	22	23	24	25	26

18	1	13	9	13	1	5	16

Roundabout

Solutions to Radial clues (1 to 24) either start from the outer edge of the circle and read inwards, or start from the inner ring and read outwards to the edge (so they are all five-letter words). Solutions to Circular clues read in either a clockwise or an anti-clockwise direction round the circle.

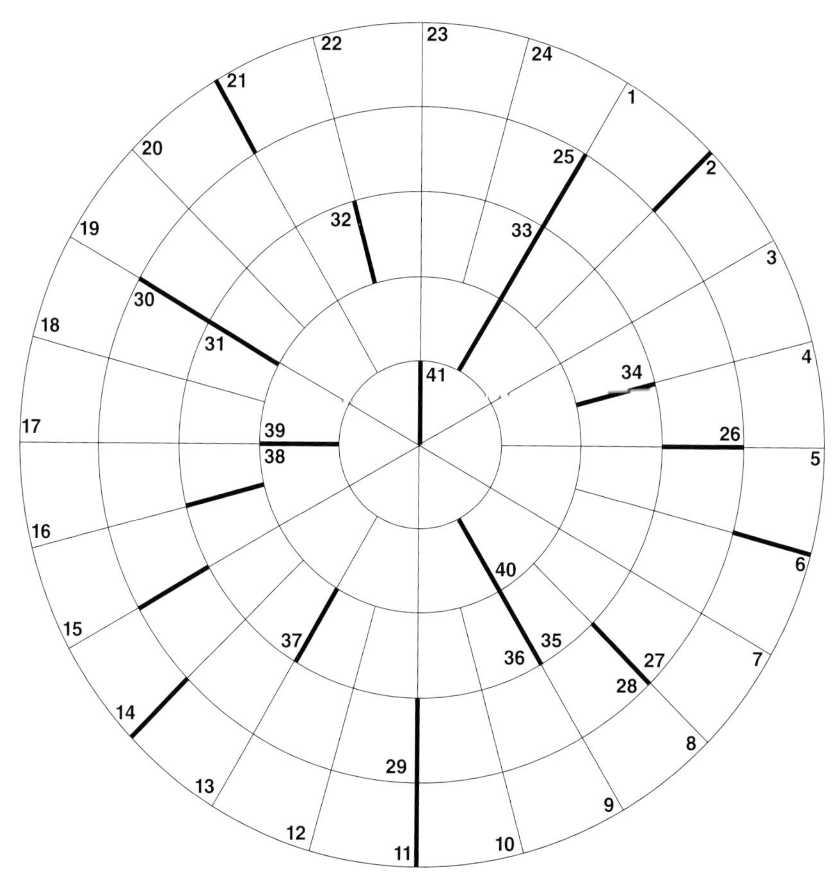

RADIAL:

INWARDS

1 Employees
2 Smell
3 Angled edge
5 Sales patter
9 Snapshot
10 Argument (3-2)
13 Tendon
15 Group of trees
16 The ones here
17 Very perceptive
19 One who presides over a meeting
21 Not intoxicated
22 Fire prodder

OUTWARDS

4 Slowly, in music
6 Minimum
7 Church instrument
8 Make a speech
11 Narrow middle part
12 Squander
14 Use scales
18 Clear upper air
20 Rampages
23 Single snooker game
24 David Jason character

CIRCULAR:

CLOCKWISE

28 Definite article
29 ___ *of the Dump*, Clive King book
36 Singer, Mr Redding
37 Pinch
39 Layer
41 Bloom

ANTI-CLOCKWISE

1 Ladder
5 Weeps
10 Parted with cash
13 Hardened
20 Relieve an itch

25 Unwrinkled
26 Canvas shelter
27 Serpent
30 Reverberate
31 Colour
32 Feather scarf
33 Acorn tree
34 By way of
35 Once more
38 Pew
40 Coral barrier

Logic Problem

Rowley Ninnett is an entrepreneur who made a vast fortune before he was forty and then retired to enjoy it. He now spends his time travelling abroad and indulging in some of his favourite pastimes. From the clues given below, can you work out where he was in each of the listed months last year, say what he was doing there, and name his female companion on each trip?

Clues

1 Rowley was gambling in Las Vegas a couple of months after the jaunt on which his companion was Lucille.

2 Mauritius was Ninnett's selected September holiday spot.

3 His chosen companion in July was Josie.

4 Annabel was Rowley's female friend on an earlier trip than the one to Honolulu, but not the one immediately preceding it.

5 Melanie was Rowley's constant beach companion on his sunbathing holiday.

6 May was the month spent playing golf, but Rowley did not spend his January holiday swimming.

7 Maria danced attendance on Rowley during his holiday in Singapore, which he did not take in March.

	Bahamas	Honolulu	Las Vegas	Mauritius	Singapore	Gambling	Golf	Scuba diving	Sunbathing	Swimming	Annabel	Josie	Lucille	Maria	Melanie
January															
March															
May															
July															
September															
Annabel															
Josie															
Lucille															
Maria															
Melanie															
Gambling															
Golf															
Scuba diving															
Sunbathing															
Swimming															

Month	Location	Activity	Companion

Pathfinder

Beginning with the letter S in the shaded square, follow a single path to find 16 English seaside towns. The trail passes through every letter once and may twist up, down and sideways (but never diagonally).

BLACKPOOL	PLYMOUTH
BUDE	SCARBOROUGH
CLACTON	SEATON
CROMER	SKEGNESS
FILEY	SOUTHPORT
LYME REGIS	SWANAGE
MORECAMBE	WEYMOUTH
NEWQUAY	WORTHING

U	T	H	P	T	S	F	I	L	E	Y
O	C	A	O	R	K	E	B	M	A	W
S	T	L	S	E	E	H	M	O	C	E
N	O	C	S	N	G	T	U	R	E	Y
B	U	D	E	L	Y	M	O	S	G	M
S	L	O	L	P	E	G	A	W	N	O
E	P	O	Y	M	E	A	N	H	I	U
A	K	C	A	L	R	E	G	T	R	T
T	O	G	H	B	B	R	I	S	O	H
C	N	U	O	R	O	A	C	S	W	Y
H	O	M	E	R	N	E	W	Q	U	A

Solutions

Wordsearch

R	F	X	Q	O	O	F	O	C	K	O	E	E	C	O	T	E	E	O	T	G
M	U	F	E	C	N	H	O	L	A	R	K	S	P	U	R	T	E	N	R	E
S	O	B	A	T	S	D	I	R	A	U	Q	A	A	T	L	E	D	E	C	R
G	N	M	Y	S	A	K	H	E	G	O	T	R	N	E	A	P	S	O	E	C
T	R	F	A	N	I	E	S	N	L	O	G	M	H	T	A	R	E	N	I	S
X	E	B	E	N	E	D	I	C	T	C	U	M	B	E	R	B	A	T	C	H
O	I	C	D	A	L	L	R	N	O	O	M	E	U	L	B	I	T	P	N	B
R	I	R	E	J	W	A	S	O	R	E	T	H	A	U	N	S	L	S	I	R
G	O	N	P	O	U	M	A	E	C	D	S	T	K	D	O	Y	R	T	T	I
Y	I	B	R	D	A	L	E	N	F	L	T	S	E	R	E	A	O	S	P	T
A	A	K	I	T	N	I	I	H	N	A	U	P	E	C	D	D	L	W	S	I
D	J	G	R	N	G	A	A	U	G	M	E	O	E	I	W	I	T	I	N	S
E	A	R	N	E	W	S	R	E	S	N	O	L	I	W	T	L	N	T	E	H
L	C	D	A	I	H	I	R	G	D	C	R	U	A	P	S	O	E	H	O	O
L	I	L	A	T	P	Y	L	E	H	G	A	T	N	M	E	H	R	I	F	P
I	S	K	O	I	E	P	N	L	Y	S	E	E	A	E	C	R	D	N	N	E
T	T	L	R	L	H	C	U	E	I	R	I	S	S	U	A	E	I	S	O	N
S	N	T	N	E	E	P	R	N	L	A	A	T	L	A	G	M	S	D	I	G
A	M	E	E	D	O	C	D	I	A	N	M	R	I	T	R	M	A	A	E	O
B	H	I	A	S	H	L	L	O	U	W	E	S	A	R	N	U	R	Y	B	L
T	Y	Y	I	S	E	Y	F	C	D	O	S	A	P	L	B	S	R	G	N	F

Suko

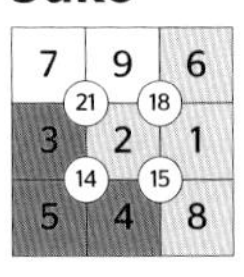

Wordsearch

S	L	P	P	A	S	J	E	X	T
G	E	L	A	E	D	A	I	B	T
G	C	L	I	N	D	O	U	A	G
E	O	R	F	N	C	R	S	C	O
L	F	I	U	F	G	A	N	O	D
E	F	S	T	E	A	R	K	N	T
K	E	R	R	I	L	W	I	E	O
A	E	E	I	N	W	O	R	B	H
H	N	H	T	O	O	B	T	P	S
S	C	J	U	K	E	B	O	X	D

Sudoku

7	2	4	6	9	3	1	8	5
1	5	6	7	8	4	2	9	3
9	3	8	2	1	5	4	6	7
5	4	3	9	6	1	7	2	8
6	7	1	3	2	8	5	4	9
2	8	9	4	5	7	3	1	6
4	6	7	1	3	9	8	5	2
3	9	5	8	4	2	6	7	1
8	1	2	5	7	6	9	3	4

Number Jig

			1	0	6	2	6	
7	5	9				2		
5				6		6	4	4
1	7	7	2	4		7		6
1		3		6	1	4	0	5
		5		1		6		1
9	3	0	0	2	3		2	
		3		6			3	
	4	7	7	2	2	7	0	

Short Code

G	N	I	S	P
A	E	O	Z	R

Dice Maze

The final dice in your trip is the blue 1, third dice down in the second column.

Linkword

FLAT, SONG, RING, HERE, SPOT, HARD, INTO **FOGHORN**

Sudoku

4	2	5	1	9	3	7	6	8
6	7	3	2	4	8	9	5	1
8	1	9	7	6	5	3	2	4
2	6	1	8	7	4	5	9	3
9	5	8	3	2	6	1	4	7
3	4	7	9	5	1	2	8	6
5	9	4	6	1	7	8	3	2
1	8	6	5	3	2	4	7	9
7	3	2	4	8	9	6	1	5

Brickwork

Add Up

89

Word Ladder

WIND, wine, wide, tide, bide, bite, KITE

Suguru

1	2	4	2	1	5	3
3	5	1	5	4	2	1
1	4	2	3	1	3	4
3	5	1	4	2	5	2
2	4	3	5	1	4	3
1	5	1	2	3	2	1
2	4	3	4	1	4	3

Solutions

Arroword

Live Aid

Kids' Corner

Honeycomb

1 Expert 2 Invert 3 Wrasse 4 Peruse 5 Vestry 6 Memory 7 Infant 8 Assent 9 Russet 10 Street 11 Modest 12 Wisest 13 Fedora 14 Scrape 15 Scrubs 16 Regale 17 Degree 18 Serape 19 Roused 20 Parted 21 Bureau 22 Landau 23 Errant 24 Patent 25 Unions 26 Recent 27 Recite 28 Netted 29 Retina 30 Tierce 31 Noddle 32 Nestle 33 Tisane 34 Ethane 35 Nitric 36 Critic 37 Doomed 38 Sonnet 39 Sonata 40 Hernia 41 Terror 42 Impact 43 Empire 44 Endure 45 Tasted 46 Indeed 47 Ordeal 48 Casual 49 Dublin 50 Strain 51 Debate 52 Delete 53 Radish 54 Banish.

Two for Tea

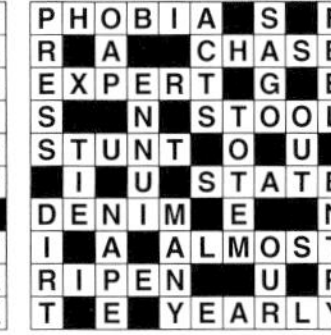

Block Party

There are 133 blocks in the pile, so 83 have been removed.

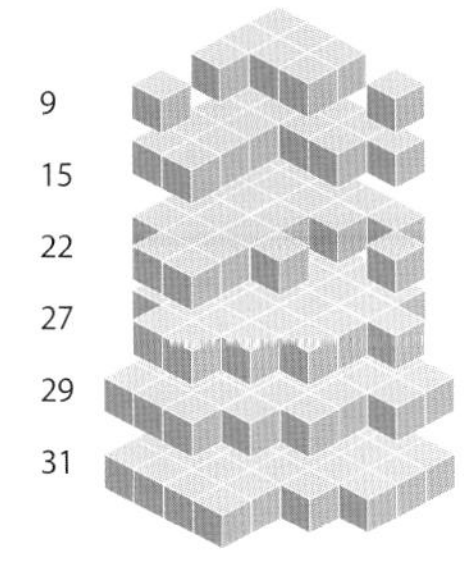

Spot the Difference

Jumbo Codeword

Potatoes

Roundabout

RADIAL: 1 Staff 2 Sniff 3 Bevel 4 Lento 5 Spiel 6 Least 7 Organ 8 Orate 9 Photo 10 Set-to 11 Waist 12 Waste 13 Sinew 14 Weigh 15 Copse 16 These 17 Acute 18 Ether 19 Chair 20 Riots 21 Sober 22 Poker 23 Frame 24 Frost. **CIRCULAR:** 1 Steps 5 Sobs 10 Spent 13 Set 20 Scratch 25 Smooth 26 Tent 27 Asp 28 The 29 Stig 30 Echo 31 Hue 32 Boa 33 Oak 34 Via 35 Again 36 Otis 37 Nip 38 Seat 39 Tier 40 Reef 41 Flower.

Logic Problem

Rowley's companion in Mauritius in September (clue 2) cannot have been Lucille (clue 1), or Annabel (clue 4), while he was with Josie in July (clue 3). Maria accompanied him in Singapore (clue 7), so it must have been Melanie who went with him to Mauritius, where they therefore spent their time sunbathing (clue 5). We now know Rowley was not sunbathing in January, nor was he swimming (clue 6), while that clue also tells us he played golf in May. Clue 1 rules out January for gambling in Las Vegas, so he must have been scuba diving in that month. We know he was not gambling in May, so his March companion was not Lucille (clue 1), nor was she Maria (clue 7). We know she was not Josie or Melanie, so she must have been Annabel. Clue 4 now rules out January, March or May for the holiday in Honolulu, and we know it did not take place in September, so it must have been the July jaunt with Josie. We know they did not spend it scuba diving, gambling, playing golf or sunbathing, so they must have spent it swimming. We have now matched months with four activities, so, by elimination, Rowley must have been gambling in Las Vegas with Annabel in March, so, from clue 1, his scuba diving holiday companion in January must have been Lucille, and, by elimination, this must have been in the Bahamas. Also by elimination, the holiday in Singapore with Maria must have taken place in May, and must have been spent playing golf. **In summary: January, Bahamas, scuba diving, Lucille. March, Las Vegas, gambling, Annabel. May, Singapore, golf, Maria. July, Honolulu, swimming, Josie. September, Mauritius, sunbathing, Melanie.**

Pathfinder

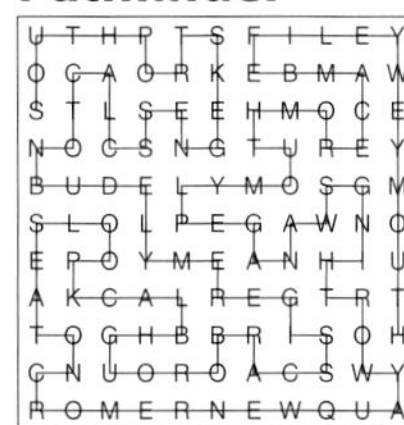

Summertime
And the living is easy,
Fish are jumpin'
And the cotton is high.

Oh, your daddy's rich
And your mama's good lookin'
So hush little baby now
don't you cry.

George Gershwin and Dubose Heyward, 'Porgy and Bess'

Wordsearch

Find all the listed words associated with the seaside.

BAY
BEACH
BOOGIE BOARD
BREAKWATER
BREEZE
BUCKET AND SPADE
BUOY
CAFE
CANDYFLOSS
CLIFF
COASTGUARD
DINGHY
DRIFTWOOD
DUNE
FERRY
FISH AND CHIPS
FISHING NET
FLIPPERS
FUNFAIR
GROYNE
HARBOUR
HEADLAND
JETTY
KISS-ME-QUICK
LANDING STAGE
LIFEBELT
LIGHTHOUSE
LOBSTER POT
MOORING
OCEAN
PADDLE
PEBBLE
PIER
PORT
QUAY
REEF
ROCK POOL
SALT
SANDCASTLE
SAUCY POSTCARD
SEAGULL
SHELL
SHINGLE
SHORE
SPEEDBOAT
SPRAY
STICK OF ROCK
TIDE
WHARF
YACHT

SATURDAY
1

SUNDAY
2

MONDAY
3

TUESDAY
4

WEDNESDAY
5

THURSDAY
6

FRIDAY
7

SATURDAY
8

Suko

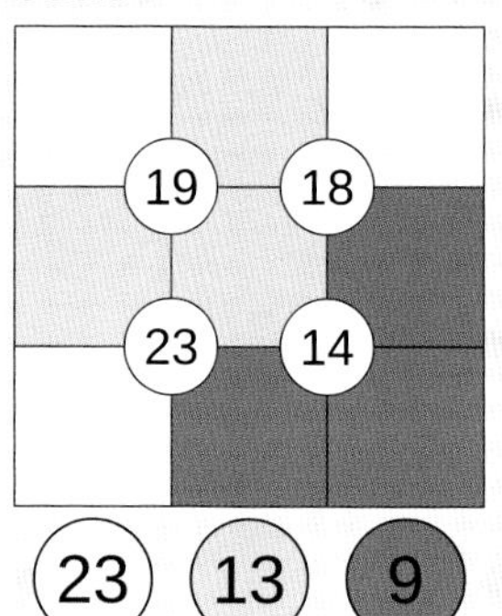

Wordsearch

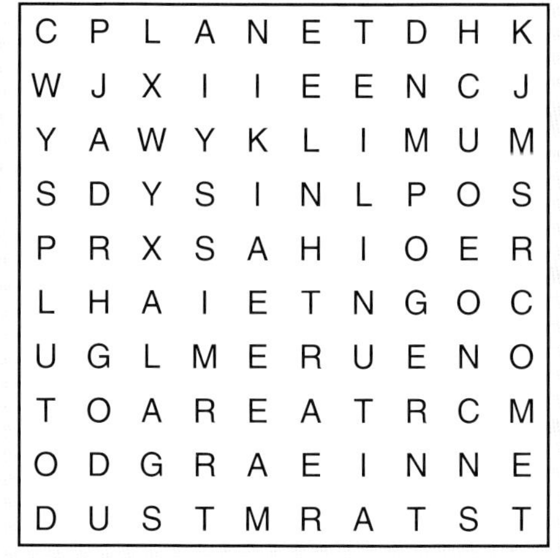

C	P	L	A	N	E	T	D	H	K
W	J	X	I	I	E	E	N	C	J
Y	A	W	Y	K	L	I	M	U	M
S	D	Y	S	I	N	L	P	O	S
P	R	X	S	A	H	I	O	E	R
L	H	A	I	E	T	N	G	O	C
U	G	L	M	E	R	U	E	N	O
T	O	A	R	E	A	T	R	C	M
O	D	G	R	A	E	I	N	N	E
D	U	S	T	M	R	A	T	S	T

COMET
DUST
EARTH
GALAXY
GAS
JUPITER
MARS
METEOR
MILKY WAY
MOON
PLANET
PLUTO
SATURN
STAR
SUN

Sudoku

8	1							
3		6						4
	9				2	3		
				4		8	5	
			3		8		6	
		4		6		1		3
		2	8		3		4	1
			2	1		7		5
	3				7	6	8	

SUNDAY
9

MONDAY
10

TUESDAY
11

WEDNESDAY
12

THURSDAY
13

FRIDAY
14

SATURDAY
15

SUNDAY
16

Number Jig

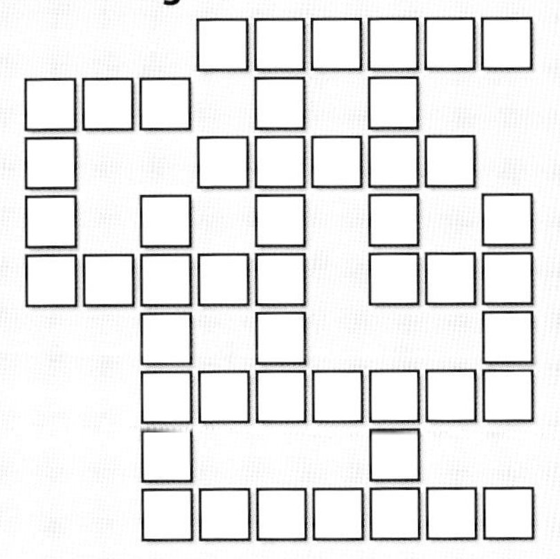

3 digits
454
582
878

4 digits
3462
8535

5 digits
14527
52528
93224

6 digits
453649
940904

7 digits
4346882
6225542
9701202

Short Code

Sum People

Each of the characters in this sum box represents a different number, with the added total of the numbers at the end of each row and column. Work out the value of each character and fill in the question mark.

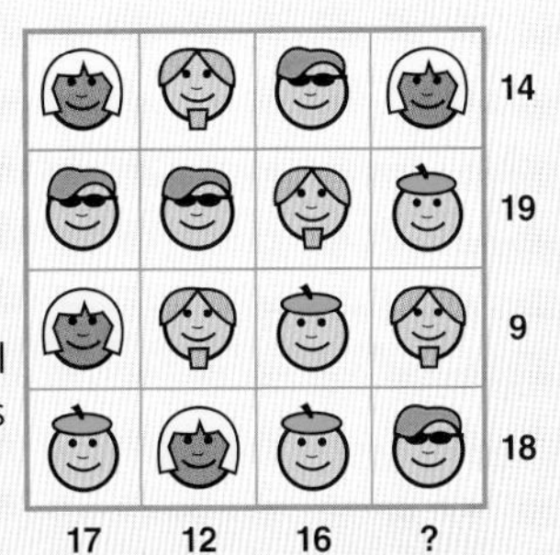

MONDAY
17

TUESDAY
18

WEDNESDAY
19

THURSDAY
20

FRIDAY
21

SATURDAY
22

SUNDAY
23

MONDAY
24

Linkword

CASH					CHART
TAX					BRAKE
LOVE					EGG
EGO					OVER
CRAZY					CLUB
VICTORIA					DUFF
GET					PROPERTY

Sudoku

	7		5		8	2		9
6		4	3					8
9				8				6
	2	7			1			
		6	7			8		1
			4	3		1		
7				2				4
	1				5	7		

Brickwork

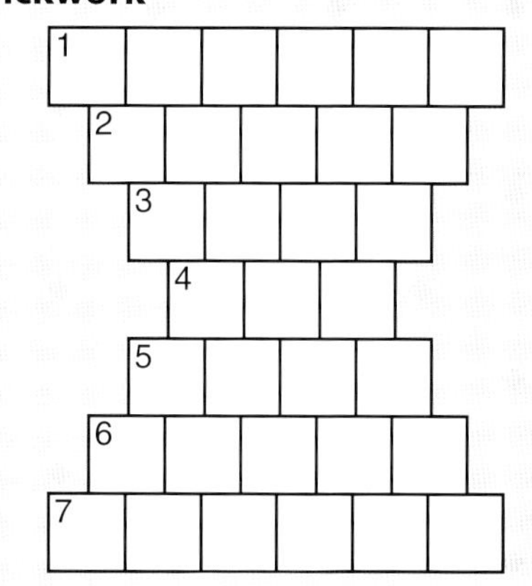

1 Sharp-tasting (6)
2 Ethnic group (5)
3 Wound from an insect (4)
4 Have a wager (3)
5 Hollow cylinder (4)
6 Savage person (5)
7 Spread for bread (6)

TUESDAY
25

WEDNESDAY
26

THURSDAY
27

FRIDAY
28

SATURDAY
29

SUNDAY
30

MONDAY *AUGUST BANK HOLIDAY*
31

Add Up

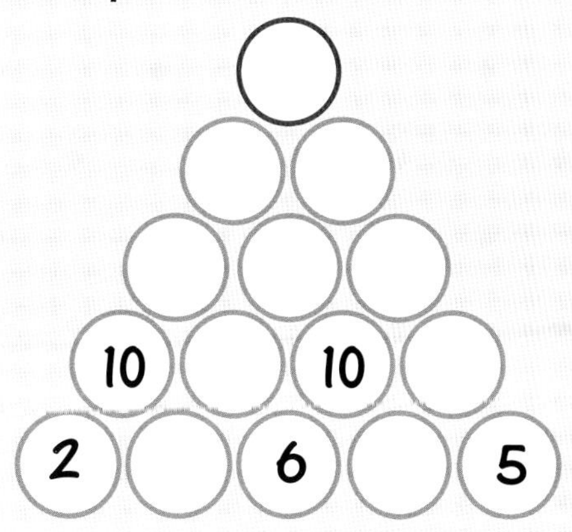

Word Ladder

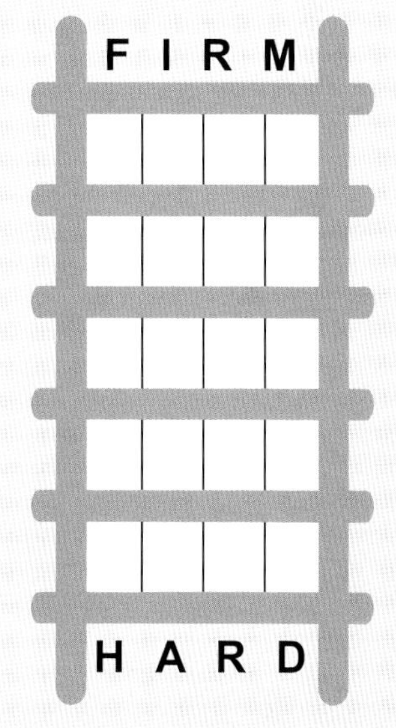

Suguru

5			3			
		4			4	
			2			
	1					
	5					

Crossword

Rearrange the letters in the shaded squares to spell out the name of a city which holds an annual festival in August.

ACROSS

1 Persian monarch (4)
6 Legally fair (4)
8 Par for the course (7)
9 Vex, annoy (3)
11 Bar pianist in *Casablanca* (3)
13 Edge forward quietly (5)
16 Remove clothes (5)
18 Course to travel (5)
19 Black or green cocktail fruit (5)
20 Once more (5)
21 Country bumpkin (5)
22 Young goats (4)
25 Deliberately disobey (4)
27 Country entry permit (4)
28 Stone particles (4)
29 Cook (in a restaurant) (4)
31 Roof slate (4)
34 Unfit, bungling (5)
37 Hat edges (5)
38 Exam already failed at least once (5)
39 Award for winning (5)
40 Unpleasantly loud (5)
43 Singing sister in the Carpenters (5)
46 Cooking vessel (3)
49 Commercial channel (inits)(3)
50 One who engages in sport purely for pleasure (7)
51 Cut with small quick strokes (4)
52 ___ log, Christmas dessert (4)

DOWN

2 Mane, locks (4)
3 Cod-like fish (4)
4 Clockwork winder (3)
5 Candle material (3)
6 In ___, as a joke (4)
7 Half-attached house (4)
10 Jog the memory of (6)
12 Covered walk with shops (6)
13 Large cape (5)
14 Something which is hunted (4)
15 Good fortune (4)
16 Marine mammal with whiskers (4)
17 ___ Black, first postal stamp (5)
23 From Dublin, perhaps (5)
24 Long thin neck warmer (5)
25 Finger or toe (5)
26 Fancy edging (5)
29 Hut made from logs (5)
30 Actress daughter of Edward Fox (6)
32 Put between (the pages) (6)
33 ___ John, singer (see picture) (5)
34 Children's 'spotting' game (1-3)
35 Leave the stage (4)
36 Long hard journey, usually on foot (4)
41 Unwrap (a present) (4)
42 Suddenly break (4)
44 Well ventilated (4)
45 Wicked, bad (4)
47 Male relation (3)
48 Doctor for animals (3)

Jigword

3 letters
ALB
ASP
EAT
HEW
HUE
NET
RAG
WAY

4 letters
FILE
GASH
NORM
ROOT
SPIN
SULK
VEIL
WIRY

5 letters
AMONG
ERODE
LUCRE
OXLIP
PLUSH
SCARY
SCUFF
SLICK
STREW
UPSET

6 letters
AFFORD
CALLUS
CONVEY
IMPALE
RASCAL
TACTIC
TALENT
VERBAL

7 letters
AGELESS
ASPIRIN
DEPLETE
DESPOIL
GLISTEN
HERSELF
MOBSTER
PROVOKE
SARCASM
SCAPULA
SNAPPER
STIPPLE
WARTHOG

8 letters
~~CARNIVAL~~
LEANNESS
LOOPHOLE
OUTHOUSE
SHEDLOAD

9 letters
AUTOPILOT
GEARSTICK
INFLATION
TEMPORARY
UNIFORMED

10 letters
BIRTHRIGHT

11 letters
CHAMBERMAID
RETRIBUTION
RITUALISTIC

Block Party

This used to be a big cube made of 216 small blocks measuring 6 by 6 by 6. If all the blocks that are not visible from this angle are present, can you work out how many have been taken away?

Wheels & Cogs

When the sunbather turns the handle as shown, does she bring out the sunshine or the storm cloud?

Two Timer

Two sets of clues to the same answers.

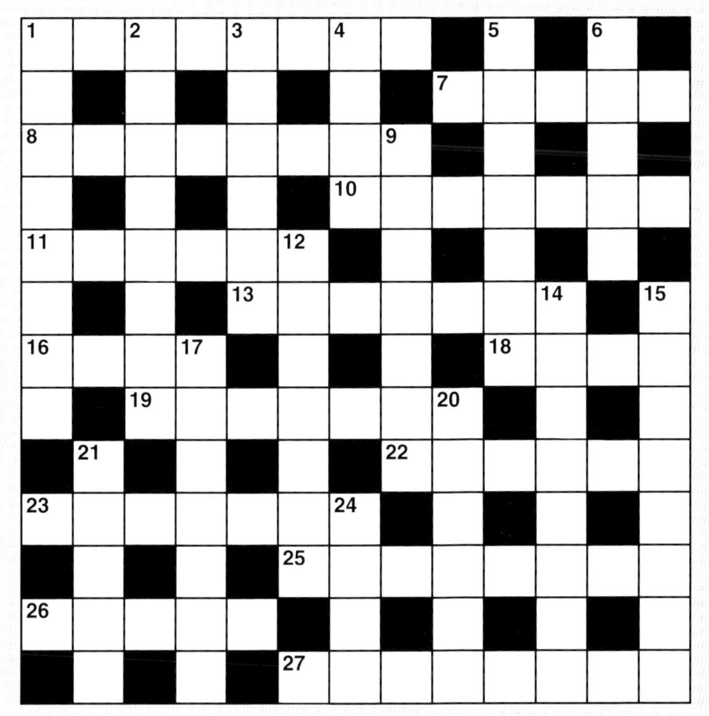

STRAIGHT CLUES

ACROSS

1 Admit that one is wrong and has been defeated (4,4)
7 Daily record of events or thoughts (5)
8 Degree of slope on a road (8)
10 Female aristocrat (7)
11 Rush, speed up (6)
13 Unwanted useless items (7)
16 Prime minister at the time of the Suez crisis (4)
18 Rear part of a plane (4)
19 Came together in support of a cause (7)
22 Brownish-red colour (6)
23 Exceptional, distinguished (7)
25 Wet-weather indicator (8)
26 Student's money (5)
27 Relating to a more affluent clientele (8)

DOWN

1 London Eye, eg (3,5)
2 More refined and stylish (8)
3 Person controlling a car (6)
4 Fairy godmother's stick (4)
5 Most eminent (7)
6 Thin slice of fried potato (5)
9 Flat-bottomed glass with no handle (7)
12 Relating to atoms (7)
14 Farmyard bundle of dried grass (8)
15 Blood component involved in clotting (8)
17 Coming into being (7)
20 Spanish chaperone (6)
21 Architectural structure which tapers to a point (5)
24 Illuminating device (4)

CRYPTIC CLUES

ACROSS

1 Surrender face up (4,4)
7 Days are numbered for this publication (5)
8 Treading dangerously on inclined surface (8)
10 Title of Dutch game (7)
11 Possesses half-score, go quickly (6)
13 Condemn rejected articles (7)
16 Garden flower (4)
18 Beastly conclusion (4)
19 Recovered on court? (7)
22 Apple for all to see rests uneasily outside (6)
23 Cooked plaice's highly regarded (7)
25 Measurement of precipitation for season in America (8)
26 Make allowances (5)
27 Rump steak, not salted initially, moving towards more expensive tastes (8)

DOWN

1 Influential person at the fair (3,5)
2 Crass lie, badly told, is nonetheless more sophisticated (8)
3 Club for the golfing motorist? (6)
4 Staff Dawn converted (4)
5 Up the longest (7)
6 Brittle part of snack (5)
9 Unsuccessful acrobat? (7)
12 Unclear about energy form (7)
14 Rick might be hiding a needle! (8)
15 Small dish of blood (8)
17 Beginning northern climb (7)
20 Governess expected lady to turn up (6)
21 High church feature (5)
24 Unclamping centre light (4)

Quiz Wordsearch

Answer the given clues and then find the answers hidden in the grid.

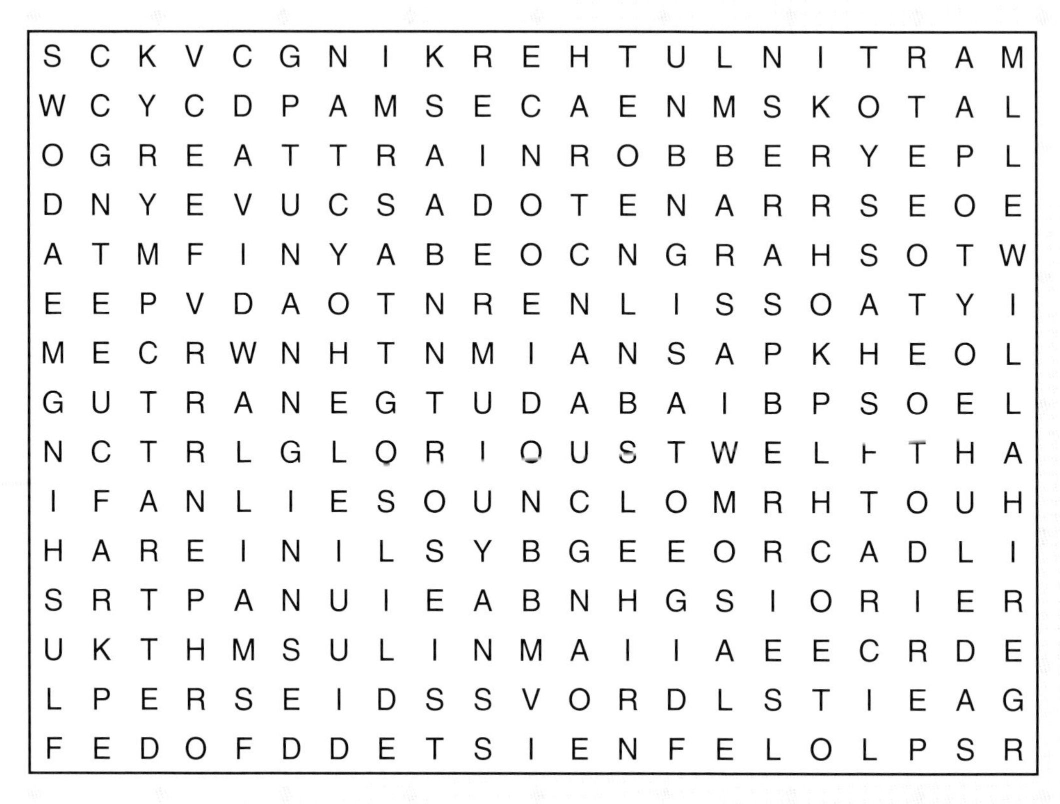

1 Annual London carnival (7,4)

2 August day which begins the grouse-shooting season (8,7)

3 *August:* _, Meryl Streep film (5,6)

4 Civil-rights leader who said 'I have a dream' on 28th August 1963 (6,6,4)

5 Ex-Spice Girl whose birthday is 6th August (4,9)

6 Female US pop star whose birthday is 16th August (7)

7 Flower of the iris family, birth flower for August (9)

8 Green semi-precious stone, August birthstone (7)

9 Infamous illegal event of August 1963 (5,5,7)

10 Meteor shower peaking in August (8)

11 Scottish city with an annual arts festival (9)

12 Small soft fruits often used in a coulis ready for picking in August (11)

13 Star of *Little Britain* whose birthday is 20th August (5,8)

14 Venue of the US Open tennis tournament (8,7)

15 Welsh festival with competitions in music, poetry and drama (10)

Logic Problem

The Inshore Rescue Boat at the popular South Coast resort of Brightbourne is kept busy every day in the summer, saving holidaymakers who get into difficulties in the shallow waters close to the coast. Yesterday, the boat saved four people. From the clues given below, can you work out who was saved at each of the listed times, what they were doing, and where they were rescued?

Clues

1 Colin Bass, who was rescued by the Brightbourne IRB at 11.00am, wasn't the person pulled from the waves off the popular West Beach.

2 The dinghy sailor whose boat was overturned by a freak wave wasn't Sally Ray, who was saved from the sea near St Anne's Rocks; the former rescue was later in the day than that of windsurfer Nina McKerrel.

3 At 2.00pm, the Brightbourne IRB picked up a holidaymaker who had got into difficulties just off Nelson Point.

4 It was a fitness-fanatic local resident whose canoe had been swamped by heavy seas who gave the IRB's crew their first job of the day.

	Colin Bass	Mike Lamprey	Nina McKerrel	Sally Ray	Canoeing	Dinghy sailing	Swimming	Windsurfing	Central Pier	Nelson Point	St Anne's Rocks	West Beach
8.00am												
11.00am												
2.00pm												
5.00pm												
Central Pier												
Nelson Point												
St Anne's Rocks												
West Beach												
Canoeing												
Dinghy sailing												
Swimming												
Windsurfing												

Rescue time	Name	Activity	Location

Jolly Mixtures

ACROSS
1 COASTERS
6 LOOT
8 MOOR
9 TRIPPERS
10 BARN
11 RANTER
13 DECO
15 AVERS
17 LACKS
19 PAGE
21 HATTER
24 ABEL
26 A SLEEP-IN
27 ARNE
28 FATE
29 ETERNITY

DOWN
2 DOURO
3 NO CREAM
4 NEED US
5 ETHER
6 PATER
7 COCAINE
12 RAPS
14 CORA
16 HAVE ICE
18 RELEARN
20 RANTED
22 LATEX
23 PETRI
25 SLATE

1	2		3		4		5	■	6		7	
■		■		■		■		■		■		■
8				■	9							
■		■		■		■		■		■		■
10				■		■	11	12				
■	■	■	13	14			■		■	■		■
15	16				■	■	■	17	18			
■		■	■		■	19	20			■	■	■
21			22		23	■		■	24		25	
■		■		■		■		■		■		■
26								■	27			
■		■		■		■		■		■		■
28				■	29							

Solutions

Wordsearch

J	S	S	O	L	F	Y	D	N	A	C	Z	B	M	Q	M	S	M	T	M	M
E	N	B	W	H	E	A	D	L	A	N	D	O	N	E	U	E	R	E	I	P
M	S	N	U	B	T	Y	G	T	B	N	I	O	T	L	I	A	N	N	M	R
K	T	U	U	C	T	R	B	N	I	R	K	G	N	B	L	G	Y	G	R	E
C	Y	O	O	T	K	E	O	S	I	C	E	I	W	B	T	U	I	N	N	E
O	Y	A	E	H	A	E	P	P	I	R	S	E	U	E	E	L	L	I	R	L
R	C	J	R	C	T	E	T	U	A	H	O	B	Z	P	M	L	S	H	S	G
F	L	E	H	P	E	H	Q	A	O	I	T	O	N	E	A	A	R	S	A	N
O	I	O	E	D	S	E	G	R	N	S	L	A	M	D	U	N	E	I	N	I
K	F	C	B	I	M	T	E	I	R	D	N	R	E	C	A	R	U	F	D	H
C	F	O	A	S	P	A	D	D	L	E	S	D	Y	H	G	N	I	D	C	S
I	A	S	S	F	T	H	C	A	Y	D	T	P	L	R	E	O	I	T	A	G
T	L	I	A	T	E	E	N	S	O	M	O	A	A	I	I	E	R	L	S	R
S	K	S	O	I	A	H	R	O	E	S	N	L	W	D	F	A	E	A	T	O
W	H	A	R	F	A	E	W	P	T	T	Y	L	O	K	E	E	F	S	L	Y
R	L	R	S	R	P	T	U	C	O	R	A	E	I	C	A	O	B	N	E	N
E	N	T	B	P	F	E	A	E	R	T	R	H	W	A	E	E	B	E	U	E
E	L	O	I	I	G	R	D	E	C	O	A	S	T	G	U	A	R	D	L	F
F	U	L	R	S	D	I	F	I	M	E	O	N	R	T	Y	A	N	B	E	T
R	F	D	I	R	T	S	P	I	H	C	D	N	A	H	S	I	F	S	L	O
U	L	A	N	D	I	N	G	S	T	A	G	E	L	O	O	P	K	C	O	R

Number Jig

			9	4	0	9	0	4
8	7	8		3		3		
5			1	4	5	2	7	
3		4		6		2		3
5	2	5	2	8		4	5	4
		3		8				6
		6	2	2	5	5	4	2
		4				8		
		9	7	0	1	2	0	2

Linkword

FLOW, DISC, NEST, TRIP, GOLF, PLUM, LOST **WISTFUL**

Sudoku

1	7	3	5	6	8	2	4	9
2	8	5	9	1	4	6	3	7
6	9	4	3	7	2	5	1	8
9	5	1	2	8	3	4	7	6
8	2	7	6	4	1	3	9	5
3	4	6	7	5	9	8	2	1
5	6	9	4	3	7	1	8	2
7	3	8	1	2	6	9	5	4
4	1	2	8	9	5	7	6	3

Short Code

C	L	I	P	■	A	L	S	O
A	■	■	A	■	P	■	A	■
P	A	S	T	O	R	A	L	■
■	L	■	R	■	I	■	S	■
■	T	A	I	L	C	O	A	T
■	A	■	O	■	O	■	■	A
T	R	O	T	■	T	A	R	N

A	T	S	C	N
R	P	L	O	I

Suko

6	1	8
7	5	4
9	2	3

19 18 23 14

Wordsearch

C	P	L	A	N	E	T	D	H	K
W	J	X	I	I	E	E	N	C	J
Y	A	W	Y	K	L	I	M	U	M
S	D	Y	S	I	N	L	P	O	S
P	R	X	S	A	H	I	O	E	R
L	H	A	I	E	T	N	G	O	C
U	G	L	M	E	R	U	E	N	O
T	O	A	R	E	A	T	R	C	M
O	D	G	R	A	E	I	N	N	E
D	U	S	T	M	R	A	T	S	T

Brickwork

BITTER
TRIBE
BITE
BET
TUBE
BRUTE
BUTTER

Add Up

91

Sum People

15

1  3  4  7 

Word Ladder

FIRM, fire, mire, mare, care, card, HARD

Sudoku

8	1	7	5	3	4	2	9	6
3	2	6	1	8	9	5	7	4
4	9	5	6	7	2	3	1	8
2	6	3	7	4	1	8	5	9
1	5	9	3	2	8	4	6	7
7	8	4	9	6	5	1	2	3
6	7	2	8	5	3	9	4	1
9	4	8	2	1	6	7	3	5
5	3	1	4	9	7	6	8	2

Suguru

5	2	5	3	1	2	1
4	3	4	2	5	4	5
1	2	1	3	1	2	1
3	4	5	2	4	5	4
2	1	3	1	3	1	2
3	4	2	4	2	4	3
1	5	3	1	3	1	2

Solutions

Crossword

Edinburgh

Quiz Wordsearch

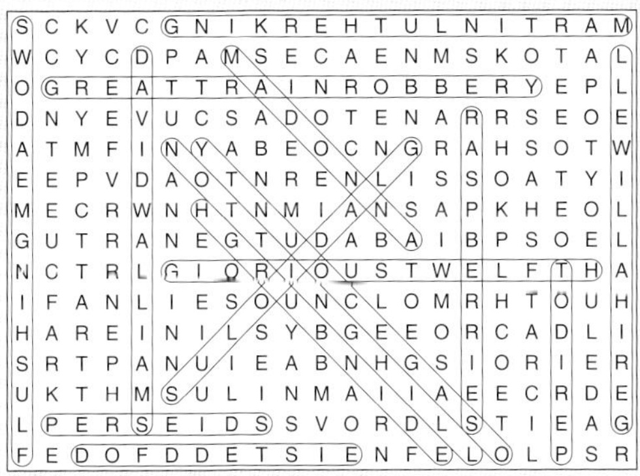

1 NOTTING HILL
2 GLORIOUS TWELFTH
3 *OSAGE COUNTY*
4 MARTIN LUTHER KING
5 GERI HALLIWELL
6 MADONNA
7 GLADIOLUS
8 PERIDOT
9 GREAT TRAIN ROBBERY
10 PERSEIDS
11 EDINBURGH
12 RASPBERRIES
13 DAVID WALLIAMS
14 FLUSHING MEADOWS
15 EISTEDDFOD

Jigword

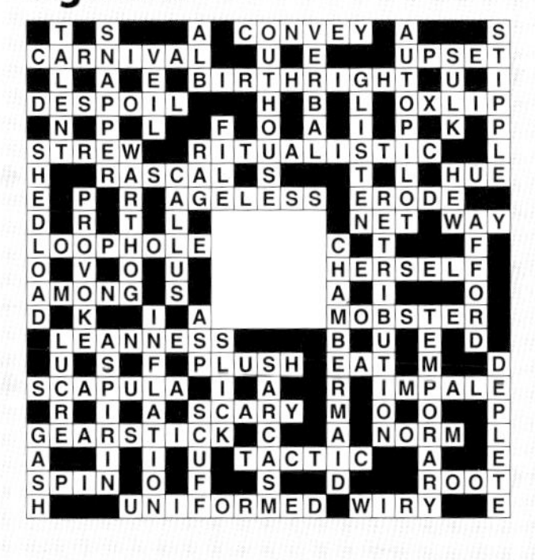

Two Timer

ACROSS: 1 Back down 7 Diary 8 Gradient 10 Duchess 11 Hasten 13 Rubbish 16 Eden 18 Tail 19 Rallied 22 Russet 23 Special 25 Rainfall 26 Grant 27 Upmarket.
DOWN: 1 Big wheel 2 Classier 3 Driver 4 Wand 5 Highest 6 Crisp 9 Tumbler 12 Nuclear 14 Haystack 15 Platelet 17 Nascent 20 Duenna 21 Spire 24 Lamp.

Block Party

There are 124 blocks in the pile, so 92 have been removed.

Wheels & Cogs

Sunshine

Logic Problem

The canoeist was saved at 8.00am (clue 4) and Nina McKerrel was the windsurfer (clue 2), so Colin Bass, who was rescued at 11.00am (clue 1) and can't have been the dinghy sailor, who was rescued later than Nina McKerrel (clue 2), must have been swimming. Sally Ray, saved at St Anne's Rocks, wasn't the dinghy sailor (clue 2), so she must have been the canoeist rescued at 8.00am and, by elimination, the dinghy sailor must have been Mike Lamprey. From clue 2, he must have been rescued at 5.00pm, and Nina McKerrel the windsurfer must have been rescued at 2.00pm at Nelson Point (clue 3). Colin Bass wasn't rescued off the West Beach (clue 1), so must have been saved at the Central Pier, leaving the West Beach rescue as the 5.00pm one of Mike Lamprey the dinghy sailor.

In summary:
8.00am, Sally Ray, canoeing, St Anne's Rocks. 11.00am, Colin Bass, swimming, Central Pier. 2.00pm, Nina McKerrel, windsurfing, Nelson Point. 5.00pm, Mike Lamprey, dinghy sailing, West Beach.

Jolly Mixtures

C	O	A	R	S	E	S	T		T	O	O	L
	D		O		N		H		A		C	
R	O	O	M		S	T	R	I	P	P	E	R
	U		A		U		E		E		A	
B	R	A	N		E		E	R	R	A	N	T
			C	O	D	E		A			I	
S	A	V	E	R				S	L	A	C	K
	C			C		G	A	P	E			
T	H	R	E	A	T		R		A	B	L	E
	I		X		R		D		R		E	
P	E	N	A	L	I	S	E		N	E	A	R
	V		L		P		N		E		S	
F	E	A	T		E	N	T	I	R	E	T	Y

By all these lovely tokens
September days are here,
With summer's best of weather
And autumn's best of cheer.

Helen Hunt Jackson

Wordsearch

Find all the listed words and phrases associated with September, together with stars celebrating their birthdays this month, hidden in the grid.

ASTER
AUTUMNAL EQUINOX
BACK TO SCHOOL
BLACKBERRIES
COURGETTES
DAMSONS
FORGET-ME-NOT
GREAT NORTH RUN
GROW YOUR OWN
HARVEST FESTIVAL
KEANU REEVES
LAST NIGHT OF THE PROMS
MARTIN FREEMAN
MICHAELMAS
OKTOBERFEST
RUGBY WORLD CUP
RUNNER BEANS
SAPPHIRE

TUESDAY
1

WEDNESDAY
2

THURSDAY
3

FRIDAY
4

SATURDAY
5

SUNDAY
6

MONDAY
7

TUESDAY
8

Suko

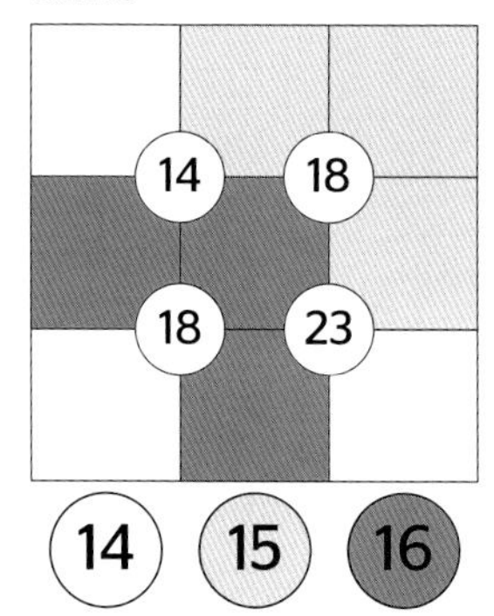

Wordsearch

B	T	E	M	P	E	R	I	N	G
L	C	A	O	C	O	C	H	D	P
E	E	A	W	S	T	N	B	A	I
N	L	N	C	L	D	U	S	R	H
D	F	I	E	A	T	I	S	K	M
E	F	M	S	T	O	U	L	O	G
T	U	B	E	N	G	T	O	O	N
I	R	R	A	A	A	L	R	S	S
H	T	P	R	R	B	E	D	E	A
W	I	N	M	I	L	K	B	S	E

BAR	CACAO TREE	SOLIDS
BEANS	COCOA	SUGAR
BLEND	DARK	TEMPERING
BLOOM	MELT	TRUFFLE
BUTTER	MILK	WHITE

Sudoku

		8		6	7	1		
	7					2		
5	1	2		4				7
		6	7				2	4
3					8			
		1	5				6	9
4	8	3		5				6
	9					4		
		7		8	1	9		

WEDNESDAY

9

THURSDAY

10

FRIDAY

11

SATURDAY

12

SUNDAY

13

MONDAY

14

TUESDAY

15

WEDNESDAY

16

Number Jig

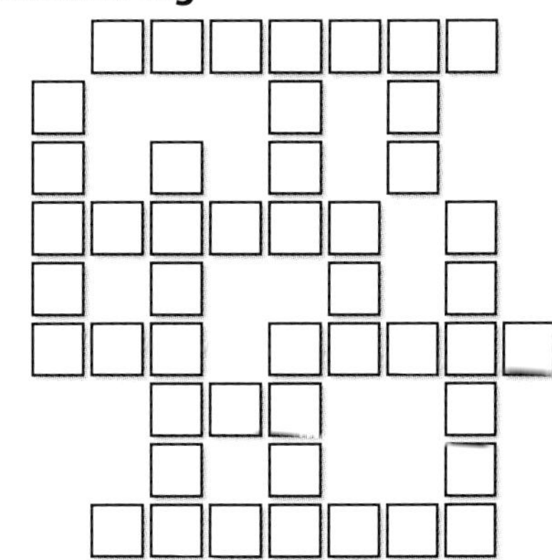

3 digits	4 digits	6 digits
411	7063	850335
515	8505	980418
571		
933		

5 digits	7 digits
81602	8827493
98844	9051568
	9845458

Short Code

Traffic Lights

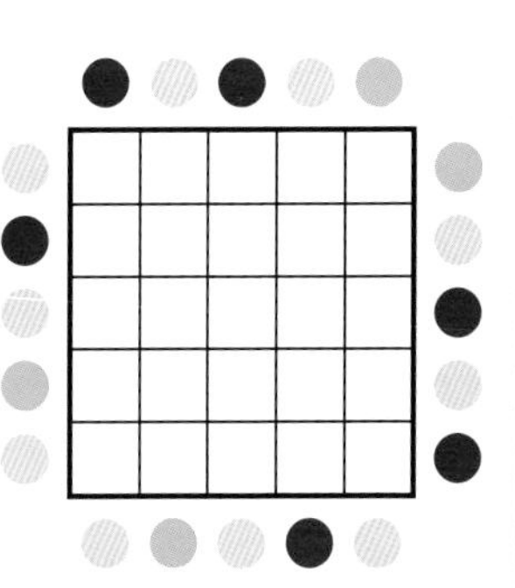

Complete the grid so that each row and column contains a red, yellow and green light. The lights at the end of each column and row tell you the colour of the first light you will meet as you move up or down the column, or side-to-side across the row.

THURSDAY
17

FRIDAY
18

SATURDAY
19

SUNDAY
20

MONDAY
21

TUESDAY
22

WEDNESDAY
23

THURSDAY
24

Linkword

BIRTH					LANGUAGE
SECOND					ROAD
FALLING					TREK
BREAK					MONEY
CHANGED					CHANGE
EMPIRE					MANAGER
ROCK					PACK

Sudoku

		2				1		
					1	5	9	
			4		2		6	8
				1	6	9	3	
9	4				7			
			5			7		
8								3
5	7			4				
4	2	3		5				

Brickwork

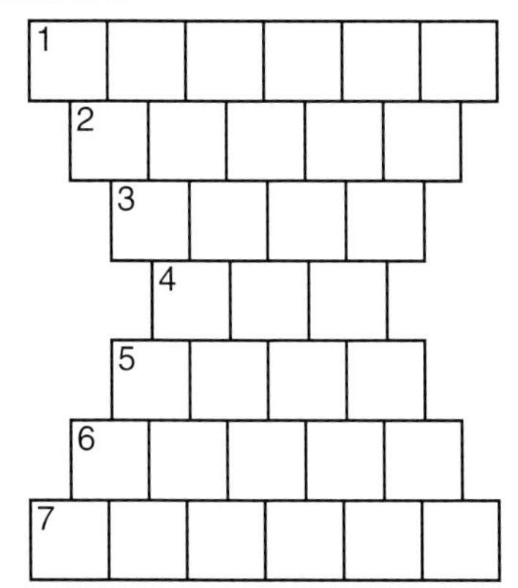

1 Taken by thieves (6)

2 Beginning, start (5)

3 Short letter (4)

4 Digit on the foot (3)

5 Officially ban (4)

6 Went to the polls (5)

7 Very religious (6)

FRIDAY
25

SATURDAY
26

SUNDAY
27

MONDAY
28

TUESDAY
29

WEDNESDAY
30

NOTES

Add Up

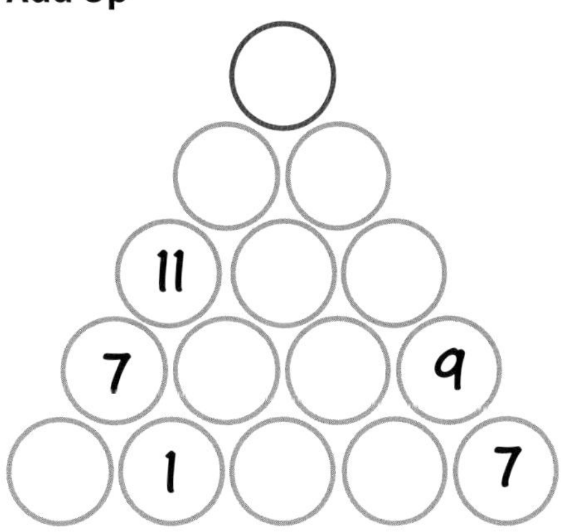

Word Ladder

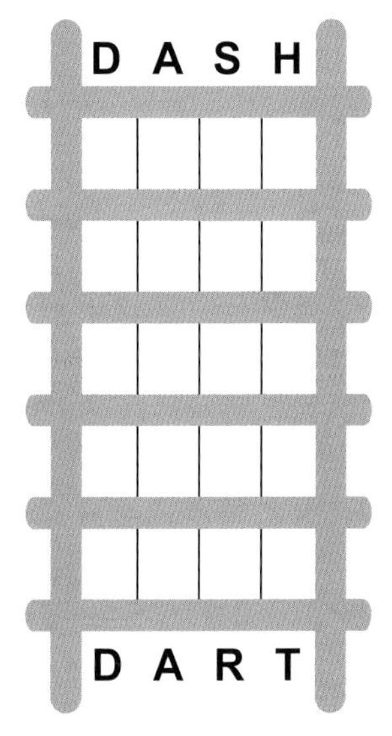

Suguru

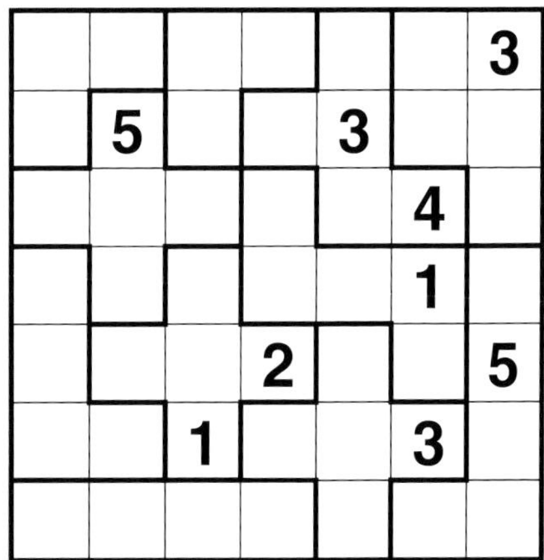

Arroword

'Red' on traffic lights
Cutting and neatening the edges of
Higher of two
Blend of two metals
Units of power
Novel by Johanna Spyri
Holiday excursion
Item of bed linen
Meadow
Design on metal
Pay for the use of something
Chum, mate
In music, a group of three players
Flightless bird (see picture)
Porridge grain
High-ranking nobleman
Naughty sprite
Sunbeam
Ghost, supernatural being
PE hall
Voucher, receipt
Small pellets of ice
Ocean movement
Jealous emotion
Officially ban
Famous pirate captain
Prima donna
Jewel
Total failure
Seem, appear
Speed of walking
Untrue statement
Practise boxing
Objects, disapproves
Makeshift boat
Compel, pressurise
State the main points again
Put (text) into cipher
Pig's home
Unlawful
Show's climax
Enthusiastic
Scold, reprimand (4,3)
Zigzag ski race
__ year, period of 366 days
Shopper's memory aid
Houses converted from stables
Anger, annoy
Blue __, small songbird
(Had) increased
Small round vegetable
Widespread disease in an area
Plant liquid
Rod for roasting meat
Do needlework
Small
Fat used to make boiled puddings
All at __, confused

Rearrange the letters in the shaded squares to spell out something that was discovered in September 1928.

Doggy Doubles

Which two of these pooches are the same?

Honeycomb

All the answers are six-letter words. Each answer is entered in a circle around its clue number. The first letter of the answer is entered in the shaded triangle immediately above the clue number. If the clue number is odd, enter the answer in an anti-clockwise direction. If the clue number is even, enter the answer in a clockwise direction.

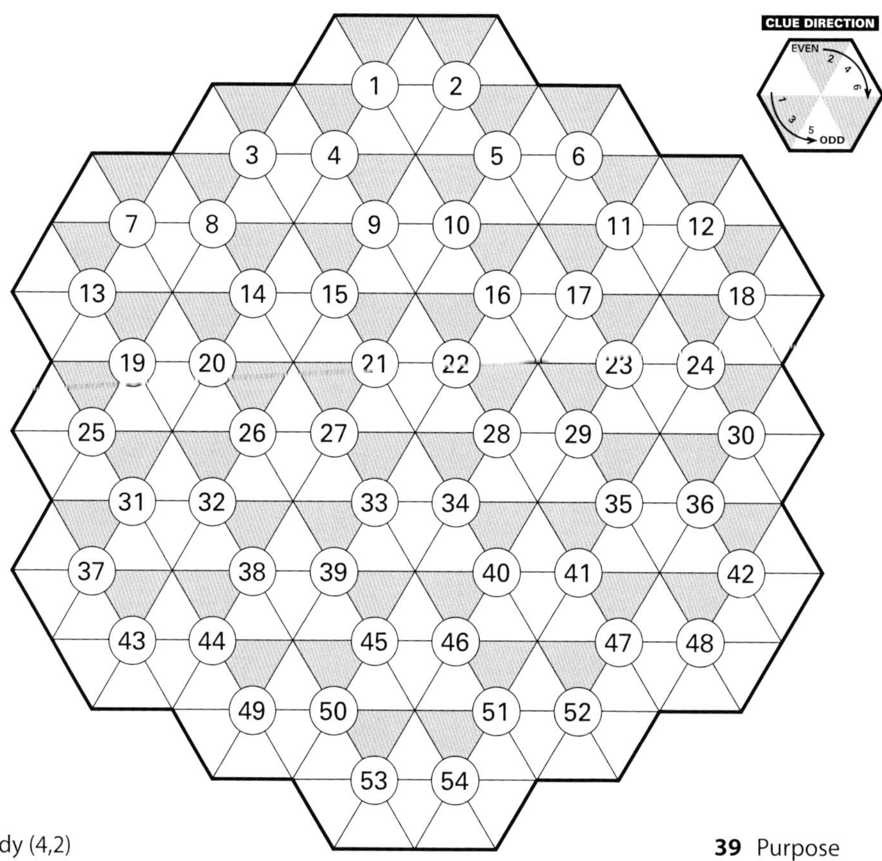

1 Trendy (4,2)
2 Even though
3 From the beginning
4 Separate grain from corn
5 Previously
6 Tolerate
7 Unassuming
8 Fine meal
9 Pang of conscience
10 Fail to remember
11 Inept person
12 Legal expert
13 Cross out
14 Central American canal
15 Male goose
16 Eager (to go)
17 Distant (3,3)
18 Cautiously
19 Poser
20 Repeating rifle or pistol
21 Inventor of the light bulb
22 Japan
23 Document case
24 Refuse
25 Wards off
26 On the condition that
27 Relations through marriage (2-4)
28 Come to a halt (4,2)
29 Quietened
30 Frustrate attempts
31 Ditch
32 Look for
33 Restaurant worker
34 Northern Ireland province
35 Most senior
36 Least common
37 Naval flag
38 Deer's horn
39 Purpose
40 Confidential
41 Crack a cipher
42 Resuscitate
43 Talented
44 In high spirits
45 Lower-level
46 Pencil rubber
47 Area of authority
48 Fiddle
49 Affirm
50 Lunge
51 Have ambition
52 Fully grown
53 Set of instructions
54 Outdoor meal

Two for Tea

ACROSS

1 Sat for a picture (5)
4 Type, kind (4)
6 ___ Brynner, actor (3)
7 Short-legged breed of dog (5)
8 Computer symbol (4)
9 Deep bell sound (5)
11 Hugh ___, British actor (5)
13 Well heeled (4)
14 Short (5)
16 Small piercing implement similar to a bodkin (3)
17 Grizzly or polar animal (4)
18 Incite (3,2)

DOWN

1 Letters after the name of a business (inits)(3)
2 Episodic story (6)
3 Expiring (5)
4 Almost fall (4)
5 One who pays rent (6)
9 Angelic child (6)
10 Simulating (6)
11 Support wall of a roof (5)
12 Burn black (4)
15 Shark appendage (3)

ACROSS

1 Insist upon (6)
6 On your own (5)
7 Cattle herder in a western (6)
9 Tell off (5)
12 Nursery ___, poem for young children (5)
14 Head monk (5)
16 Release (a knot) (5)
19 Not in a position (to) (6)
21 Person who gives blood (5)
22 Time-telling word (6)

DOWN

1 Room's furnishing scheme (5)
2 Cut (grass) (3)
3 24-hour periods (4)
4 Lead singer of pop group U2 (4)
5 Provide (money) temporarily in return for payment of interest (4)
8 Disney deer film (5)
10 Dangerous snake (5)
11 Lavatory (3)
13 Chicken (3)
15 Sharp pinch (5)
16 Release (a knot) (4)
17 Extremely small (4)
18 Ireland's currency unit (4)
20 Audience's cry of disapproval (3)

Fraction Statlons

Can you determine what fraction of the dots in this design is yellow and what percentage of them is orange?

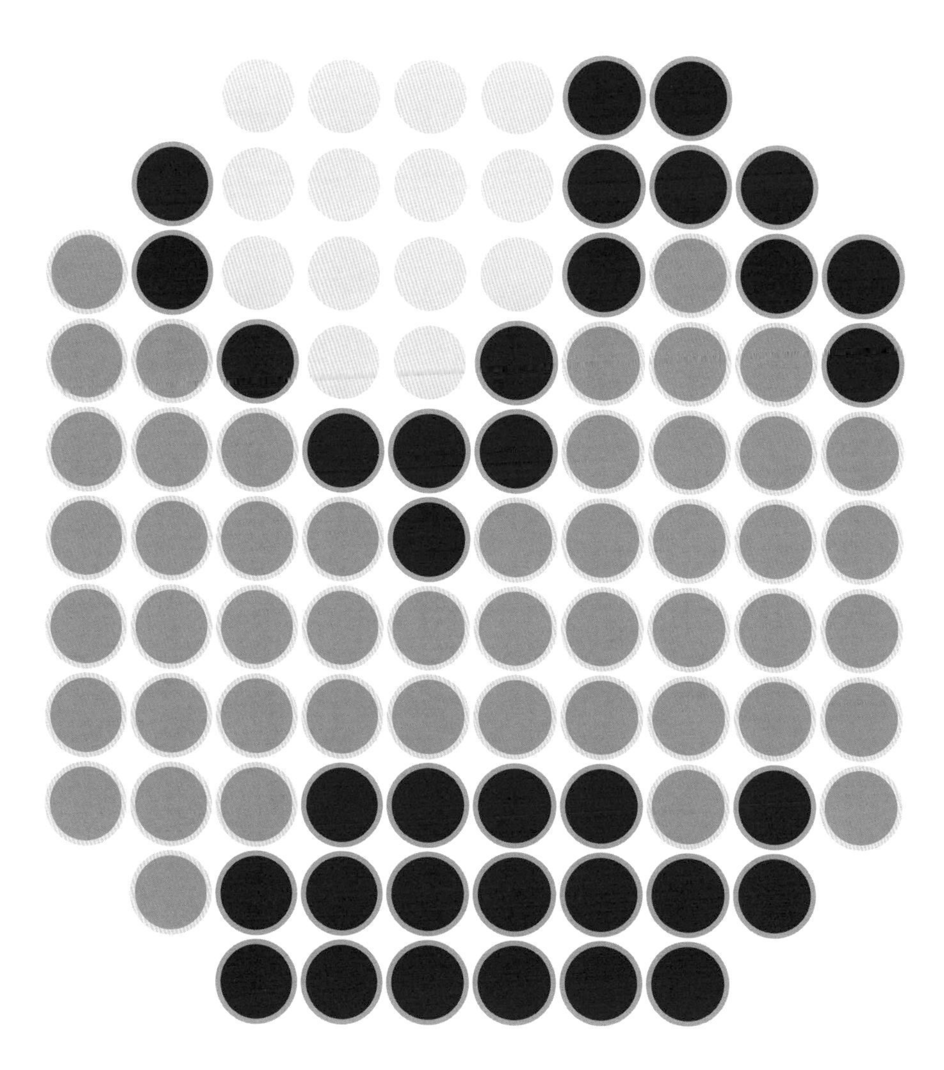

Jumbo Codeword

The letters in the phrase box will spell out the name of a festival day in September.

14	16	23	14	9	14	19	■	12	14	6	12	9
6	■	3	■	■	19	10	4	9	■	10	■	15
6 T	3 O	11 R	■	16	12	12	■	14	13	3	■	14
14	■	14	25	12	■	14	11	19	■	15	11	9
19	3	17	■	5	■	26	14	6	■	13	■	19
20	■	17	6	12	23	■	24	■	17	10	3	12
■	5	■	12	16	12	23	12	9	6	■	7	■
1	4	17	19	■	16	■	1	■	12	■	22	■
■	11	■	10	3	3	21	■	5	12	2	12	1
■	6	■	9	■	9	3	6	■	26	■	19	■
8	15	14	4	16	■	12	14	11	9	■	6	■
■	3	■	19	■	1	■	20	■	12	5	12	11
■	17	■	14	4	11	16	12	17	17	■	1	■
19	3	25	16	■	3	■	9	3	17	12	■	17
14	■	3	■	6	3	26	■	16	■	9	4	26
11	3	12	■	14	26	12	■	5	4	14	■	14
12	■	21	3	7	■	19	15	12	■	23	14	11
17	■	15	■	7	4	14	17	■	■	12	■	12
17	14	16	6	18	■	9	12	12	1	16	12	1

A B C D E F G H I J K L M N ~~O~~ P Q ~~R~~ S ~~T~~ U V W X Y Z

1	2	3	4	5	6	7	8	9	10	11	12	13
		O			T					R		
14	**15**	**16**	**17**	**18**	**19**	**20**	**21**	**22**	**23**	**24**	**25**	**26**

23	4	19	10	14	12	16	23	14	17

Roundabout

Solutions to Radial clues (1 to 24) either start from the outer edge of the circle and read inwards, or start from the inner ring and read outwards to the edge (so they are all five-letter words). Solutions to Circular clues read in either a clockwise or an anti-clockwise direction round the circle.

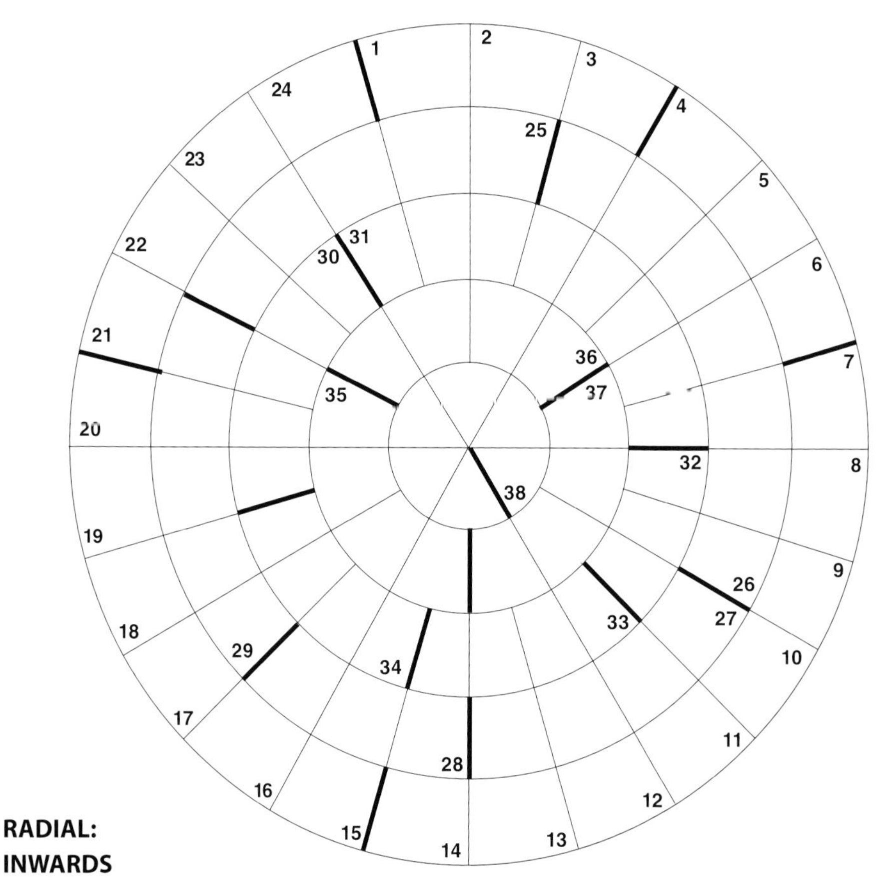

RADIAL:

INWARDS

1 Purple flowering shrub
4 Playground chute
5 Home, dwelling
6 Cut in two
7 Operate a vehicle
12 Wood-smoothing blade
13 New England state
16 Threaded, tied
17 Uncovered, exposed
18 Lose vital fluid
19 Lubricated
20 Form on a loom
23 Nimble, sprightly

OUTWARDS

2 Stop
3 Gave up
8 Satirical show
9 Fully prepared
10 Beatles' drummer
11 Opponent
14 Premium Bond selector
15 Rub out
21 Happening, occurrence
22 More senior
24 Kept behind bars

CIRCULAR: CLOCKWISE

1 Went in front
27 Swimming competition
28 Savings scheme (inits)
29 Extraterrestrial being
31 Tall garden flowers
32 Small commercial vehicle
33 Conceited
34 Land measure
37 Blood vessel

ANTI-CLOCKWISE

6 Possesses
14 Gave a job to
20 Move unsteadily
24 Devon river
25 Blockade of a town
26 Hard-wearing
30 Perfect
35 Change direction suddenly
36 Business agreement
38 Flow back

Logic Problem

Miss Raffles was very fond of her brother Arthur – A J Raffles, famous as a cricketer and as the Amateur Cracksman – so, when at the end of the 19th century the Ryerson brothers, publishers of the *Daily Messenger*, launched a campaign of vilification against Arthur and the other members of the MCC touring team which had been beaten by the Australians, she took her revenge by robbing each of them. From the clues given, can you work out where she robbed each brother, what she stole from him and what it was worth?

Clues

1 The theft from one of the Ryersons while he was staying at the County Hotel in Manchester did not bring Miss Raffles loot worth £14,000, but her loot from that job was worth more than the bullion she stole from Ranulph Ryerson.

2 The loot which Miss Raffles took from Ribston Ryerson was worth exactly ten thousand pounds more than she took from one of his brothers in the form of stocks and bonds.

3 It was cash that Miss Raffles stole in Cardiff, but not to the value of £24,000, and the brother she took it from was not Rudyard Ryerson.

4 The painting worth £10,000 wasn't stolen in Lincoln.

5 The loot from Miss Raffles' Edinburgh robbery brought her £12,000.

6 It was Redvers Ryerson's palatial holiday home in Bristol that Miss Raffles raided in revenge against his paper's insults to her brother.

	Bristol	Cardiff	Edinburgh	Lincoln	Manchester	Bullion	Cash	Jewels	Painting	Stocks and bonds	£10,000	£12,000	£14,000	£20,000	£24,000
Ranulph															
Redvers															
Ribston															
Rowland															
Rudyard															
£10,000															
£12,000															
£14,000															
£20,000															
£24,000															
Bullion															
Cash															
Jewels															
Painting															
Stocks and bonds															

Brother	Robbed in	Item	Value

Pathfinder

Beginning with the letter H in the shaded square, follow a single path to find 19 composers. The trail passes through every letter once and may twist up, down and sideways (but never diagonally).

BACH
BEETHOVEN
BERLIOZ
BIZET
BRAHMS
BRITTEN
DEBUSSY
DELIUS
ELGAR
GRIEG
HAYDN
HOLST
PURCELL
SIBELIUS
STRAUSS
STRAVINSKY
VERDI
VIVALDI
WAGNER

H	M	S	W	A	G	N	E	R	R	A
A	R	N	E	V	O	H	T	S	T	V
T	B	B	S	Y	E	L	E	S	L	I
E	Z	I	S	R	A	G	E	I	L	N
H	O	L	U	V	E	I	B	B	E	S
S	U	S	B	E	R	D	L	E	C	K
S	I	T	G	D	S	U	I	U	R	Y
T	L	E	R	I	I	H	A	P	N	E
R	A	D	G	E	D	L	Y	D	N	T
S	U	C	H	R	L	A	V	I	B	T
S	D	A	B	E	I	O	Z	V	R	I

Solutions

Wordsearch

X	Q	L	D	D	I	Y	D	I	I	L	D	I	L	I	P	Y	C	L	N	D
L	I	I	A	L	T	S	E	F	R	E	B	O	T	K	O	N	A	W	A	E
C	D	I	E	V	P	A	L	N	E	I	A	Y	E	C	U	S	O	M	D	L
G	N	I	S	A	I	H	E	N	E	A	I	L	P	R	T	R	S	A	W	E
C	A	D	T	A	N	T	I	E	S	L	O	G	H	N	U	H	T	R	A	E
N	I	U	Y	S	E	O	S	C	D	A	L	T	I	O	R	T	P	T	N	I
E	A	B	T	S	O	R	E	E	T	H	R	G	Y	L	I	F	G	I	N	M
K	S	S	A	U	E	C	D	S	F	O	H	W	K	V	O	O	R	N	T	R
I	E	A	A	E	M	N	F	L	N	T	O	S	R	R	E	O	L	F	P	U
A	T	A	W	M	T	N	I	T	O	R	S	H	G	N	Y	U	O	R	E	N
C	T	D	N	L	L	S	A	F	G	R	G	E	A	M	O	B	O	E	E	N
I	E	T	N	U	A	E	T	L	R	E	T	S	V	O	L	I	H	E	T	E
N	G	E	C	D	R	H	A	A	E	M	H	R	U	R	P	S	C	M	E	R
O	R	I	L	G	E	E	A	H	E	Q	T	G	N	M	A	E	S	A	R	B
F	U	S	K	P	O	I	E	N	C	Y	U	A	B	E	C	H	O	N	D	E
N	O	T	R	L	R	H	O	V	E	I	S	I	U	A	I	O	T	A	N	A
T	C	O	E	P	R	T	W	V	E	A	M	L	N	G	S	I	K	S	M	N
E	M	O	C	D	N	R	T	A	E	S	I	S	H	O	L	O	C	T	U	S
S	E	A	S	E	I	R	R	E	B	K	C	A	L	B	X	N	A	E	R	B
R	U	G	B	Y	W	O	R	L	D	C	U	P	T	Y	I	S	B	R	E	F
C	D	S	N	O	S	M	A	D	O	A	S	A	P	P	H	I	R	E	P	L

Suko

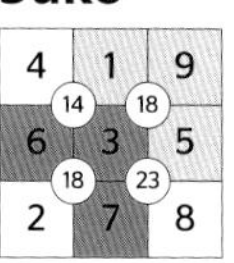

Wordsearch

B	T	E	M	P	E	R	I	N	G
L	C	A	O	C	O	C	H	D	P
E	E	A	W	S	T	N	B	A	I
N	L	N	C	L	D	U	S	R	H
D	F	I	E	A	T	I	S	K	M
E	F	M	S	T	O	U	L	O	G
T	U	B	E	N	G	T	O	O	N
I	R	R	A	A	A	L	R	S	S
H	T	P	R	R	B	E	D	E	A
W	I	N	M	I	L	K	B	S	E

Sudoku

9	3	8	2	6	7	1	4	5
6	7	4	1	9	5	2	3	8
5	1	2	8	4	3	6	9	7
8	5	6	7	1	9	3	2	4
3	4	9	6	2	8	5	7	1
7	2	1	5	3	4	8	6	9
4	8	3	9	5	2	7	1	6
1	9	5	3	7	6	4	8	2
2	6	7	4	8	1	9	5	3

Number Jig

	8	8	2	7	4	9	3	
9				0		3		
8		9		6		3		
8	5	0	3	3	5		9	
4		5			7		8	
4	1	1		8	1	6	0	2
		5	1	5			4	
		6		0			1	
	9	8	4	5	4	5	8	

Short Code

S	W	A	T	■	H	I	R	E
■	H	■	R	E	A	R	■	E
R	O	T	A	■	T	E	A	R
E	■	■	C	■	C	■	■	I
S	O	O	T	■	H	A	T	E
I	■	R	O	S	E	■	A	■
T	I	E	R	■	T	A	R	T

T	S	O	E	A
W	I	H	C	R

Traffic Lights

Linkword

SIGN, SLIP, STAR, EVEN, GEAR, LINE, FACE **NIRVANA**

Sudoku

6	3	2	9	8	5	1	4	7
7	8	4	3	6	1	5	9	2
1	9	5	4	7	2	3	6	8
2	5	7	8	1	6	9	3	4
9	4	6	2	3	7	8	1	5
3	1	8	5	9	4	7	2	6
8	6	1	7	2	9	4	5	3
5	7	9	6	4	3	2	8	1
4	2	3	1	5	8	6	7	9

Brickwork

STOLEN
ONSET
NOTE
TOE
VETO
VOTED
DEVOUT

Add Up

43

Word Ladder

DASH, bash, bask, bark, dark, darn, DART

Suguru

3	2	1	2	1	4	3
1	5	3	5	3	5	1
3	4	1	4	2	4	2
1	2	3	5	3	1	3
4	5	4	2	4	2	5
2	3	1	5	1	3	1
1	4	2	3	2	4	2

Arroword

Penicillin

Kids' Corner

Dogs 1 and 4 are the same.

Honeycomb

1 With it 2 Albeit 3 Afresh 4 Thresh 5 Before 6 Endure 7 Modest 8 Repast 9 Regret 10 Forget 11 Duffer 12 Lawyer 13 Delete 14 Panama 15 Gander 16 Raring 17 Far off 18 Warily 19 Teaser 20 Mauser 21 Edison 22 Nippon 23 Folder 24 Litter 25 Averts 26 Unless 27 In-laws 28 Pull up 29 Lulled 30 Thwart 31 Trench 32 Search 33 Waiter 34 Ulster 35 Eldest 36 Rarest 37 Ensign 38 Antler 39 Intent 40 Secret 41 Decode 42 Revive 43 Gifted 44 Elated 45 Nether 46 Eraser 47 Domain 48 Violin 49 Attest 50 Thrust 51 Aspire 52 Mature 53 Rubric 54 Picnic.

Two for Tea

Fraction Stations

There are 98 dots in the design. 14 of them (one seventh) are yellow and 49 of them (50%), are orange.

Jumbo Codeword

Michaelmas

Roundabout

RADIAL: 1 Lilac 2 Cease 3 Ceded 4 Slide 5 Abode 6 Halve 7 Drive 8 Revue 9 Ready 10 Ringo 11 Rival 12 Plane 13 Maine 14 Ernie 15 Erase 16 Laced 17 Bared 18 Bleed 19 Oiled 20 Weave 21 Event 22 Elder 23 Agile 24 Caged.

CIRCULAR: 1 Led 6 Has 14 Employed 20 Wobble 24 Dart 25 Siege 26 Durable 27 Gala 28 ISA 29 Alien 30 Ideal 31 Gladioli 32 Van 33 Vain 34 Acre 35 Veer 36 Deal 37 Vein 38 Recede.

Logic Problem

From clue 2, the stocks and bonds must have been worth £10,000 or £14,000, but it was the painting that was worth £10,000 (clue 4), so the stocks and bonds must have been worth £14,000, and the loot stolen from Ribston must have been worth £24,000 (clue 2). Therefore Ribston can't have lost the cash stolen in Cardiff (clue 3), the bullion, which was stolen from Ranulph (clue 1), and we know it can't have been the stocks and bonds or the painting, so it must have been the jewels. The Edinburgh loot was worth £12,000 (clue 5), so can't have been the jewels, the stocks and bonds or the painting, and we know the cash was stolen in Cardiff, so the Edinburgh loot must have been the bullion, which was stolen from Ranulph (clue 1). By elimination, the cash stolen in Cardiff must have been worth £20,000. It wasn't taken from Ribston, who we know lost jewels worth £24,000, Rudyard (clue 3) or Redvers, who was robbed in Bristol (clue 6), so it must have been Rowland. Since the Manchester loot can't have been worth £10,000 or £14,000 (clue 1), it must have been worth £24,000, and was therefore Ribston's jewels. By elimination, Rudyard must have been robbed in Lincoln. He can't have lost loot worth £10,000 (clue 4), so it must have been worth £14,000, and was therefore stocks and bonds, leaving Redvers, robbed in Bristol, as the man who was robbed of a painting worth £10,000.

Ranulph, Edinburgh, bullion, £12,000. Redvers, Bristol, painting, £10,000. Ribston, Manchester, jewels, £24,000. Rowland, Cardiff, cash, £20,000. Rudyard, Lincoln, stocks and bonds, £14,000.

Pathfinder

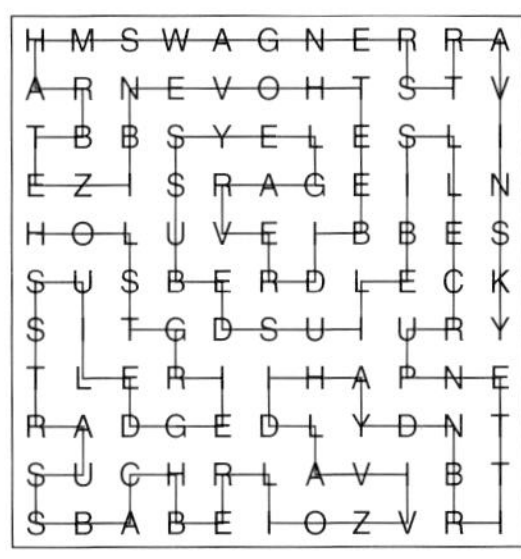

October

The falling leaves drift by the window
The autumn leaves of red and gold
I see your lips, the summer kisses,
The sunburned hands I used to hold.
Since you went away the days grow long
And soon I'll hear old winter's song
But I miss you most of all my darling
When autumn leaves start to fall.

Claudio Merlini

Wordsearch

Find all the listed words associated with Halloween.

BANDAGE
BAT
BLACK CAT
BROOMSTICK
CAULDRON
COBWEB
COFFIN
COSTUME
COVEN
CREAKY DOOR
CREEPY
DEMON
DEVIL
EERIE
FACE PAINT
FAKE BLOOD
FANCY DRESS
FANGS
GHOUL
GOOSEBUMPS
GRAVEYARD
HALLOWEEN
HAUNTED HOUSE
HOWL
KNOCK ON DOORS
LANTERN
MASK
MIDNIGHT
MONSTER
MUMMY
NIGHTFALL
OCCULT
OGRE
PARTY
PHANTOM
POINTED HAT
PUMPKIN
SCREAM
SKELETON
SKULL
SPIDER
SPOOKY
SUPERNATURAL
SWEETS
TRICK OR TREAT
VAMPIRE
WARLOCK
WEREWOLF
WITCH
ZOMBIE

THURSDAY
1

FRIDAY
2

SATURDAY
3

SUNDAY
4

MONDAY
5

TUESDAY
6

WEDNESDAY
7

THURSDAY
8

Suko

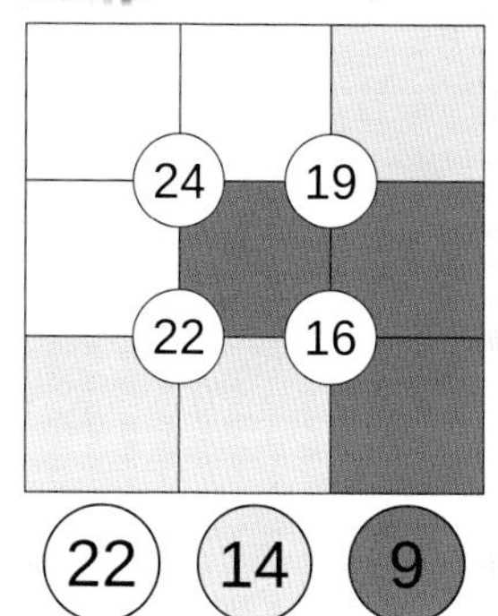

Wordsearch

D	B	E	E	T	L	E	L	E	E
G	K	Y	W	N	O	O	B	A	B
W	S	I	P	P	N	F	S	E	P
A	D	E	P	P	E	I	F	N	E
L	K	I	S	R	U	F	B	S	E
L	H	R	R	O	A	P	U	A	H
A	T	E	I	R	O	H	N	M	S
B	T	U	I	L	E	M	N	A	R
Y	I	G	A	G	L	E	Y	L	N
M	O	T	T	E	R	S	D	L	O

BABOON
BEETLE
BUNNY
DEER
EEL
FERRET
GIRAFFE
HIPPO
KRILL
LLAMA
MOOSE
OTTER
PUPPY
SHEEP
WALLABY

Sudoku

	8	6				5	7	
			6		4			
		1	7		8	4		
		9				3		
	3		2		5		9	
8	2	7		4		1	6	5
1	5		9	6	3		4	7
7								2

FRIDAY
9

SATURDAY
10

SUNDAY
11

MONDAY
12

TUESDAY
13

WEDNESDAY
14

THURSDAY
15

FRIDAY
16

Number Jig

3 digits
618
625
648
905

4 digits
4060
7880

5 digits
67500
87372

6 digits
513204
557447

7 digits
8170255
8815537
9830525

Short Code

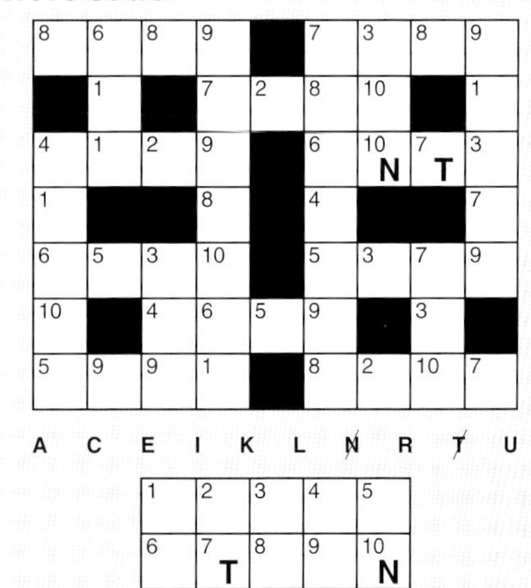

Safecracker

To open the safe, all 20 of the buttons must be pressed in the correct order (which is indicated by the numbers and directions on the buttons) before the "open" button is pressed. Which button is the first you must press in your sequence?

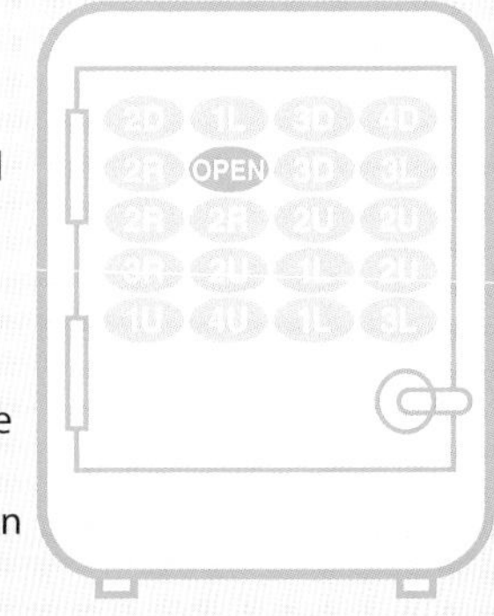

SATURDAY
17

SUNDAY
18

MONDAY
19

TUESDAY
20

WEDNESDAY
21

THURSDAY
22

FRIDAY
23

SATURDAY
24

Linkword

DEAD					RASH
CAST					OXIDE
SADDLE					DISH
FLIP					PLATE
TUNING					OUT
SUGAR					ROOT
ALARM					TENT

Sudoku

3	6		9			5	2	
					7	9	3	4
	1	8		7	5			
	4					6		
	5	2		3	4			
					9	7	1	2
8	9		7			4	5	

Brickwork

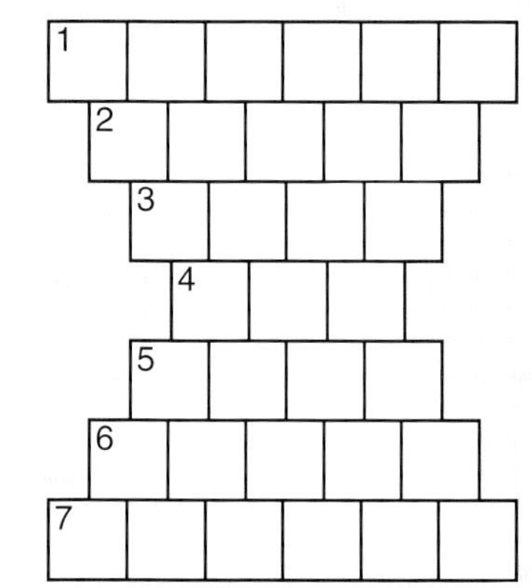

1 Girl, young woman (6)

2 Correct an error (5)

3 Give a title to (4)

4 *Homo sapiens* (3)

5 Blasted, flipping (4)

6 Wanderer (5)

7 Jam fruit (6)

SUNDAY *BRITISH SUMMER TIME ENDS*

25

MONDAY

26

TUESDAY

27

WEDNESDAY

28

THURSDAY

29

FRIDAY

30

SATURDAY *HALLOWE'EN*

31

Add Up

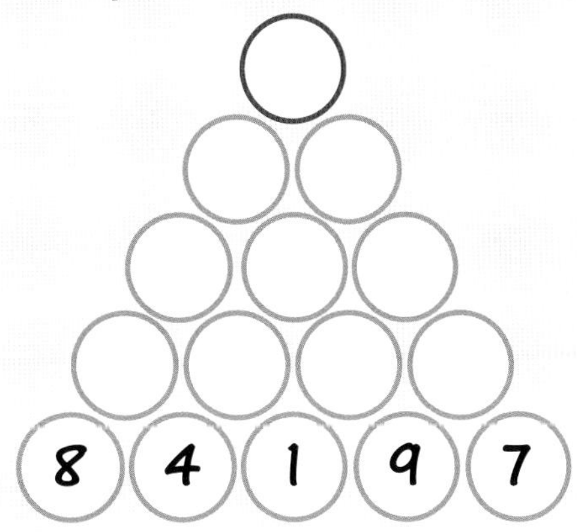

Word Ladder

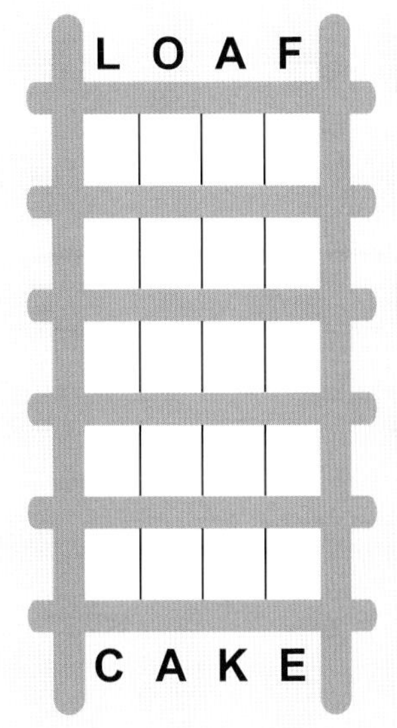

Suguru

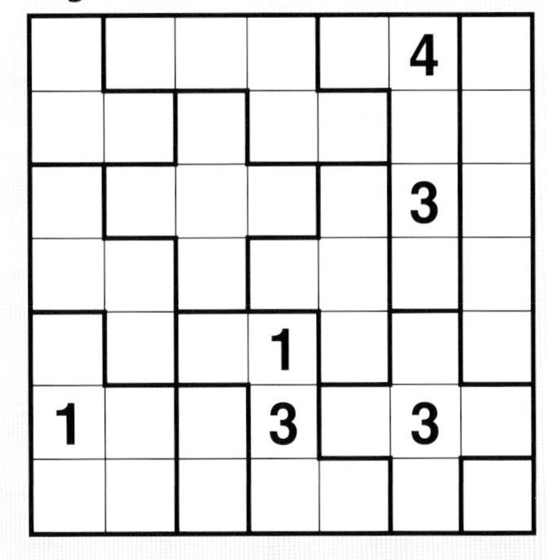

Crossword

Take the letters in the shaded squares to spell out something commonly seen in October.

ACROSS

1 Alluring seductress (4)
6 Camel's feature (4)
8 Conjure up in your mind (7)
9 Measure of current (3)
11 ___ Angeles, US city (3)
13 Brutal, heartless (5)
16 Middle traffic light (5)
18 Message sent online (5)
19 Beginning, start (5)
20 Crook's false name (5)
21 Surface gloss (5)
22 Outer covering of the body (4)
25 Stuff, kit (4)
27 Opposite of 'easy' (4)
28 Bus running on tracks (4)
29 Clever ploy (4)
31 ___ *in Boots*, pantomime (4)
34 Hot sweet drink made with whisky (5)
37 Tree or implement of corporal punishment (5)
38 Privileged group (5)
39 Artist's picture support (5)
40 Absorbent towel for a baby's bottom (5)
43 Scalp-dwelling parasite (5)
46 Hair goo! (3)
49 ___ Shannon, singer of *Runaway* in 1961 (3)
50 In a ship (2,5)
51 Homer Simpson's son (4)
52 Traditional Japanese wrestling (4)

DOWN

2 Slightly open (4)
3 Copper tube for water (4)
4 Legal system (3)
5 That bloke's (3)
6 Position from which you steer a boat (4)
7 Poet's inspiring genius (4)
10 Dish of oats, nuts and fruit (6)
12 Do a favour (6)
13 Annoyed (5)
14 ___ *Twist Again*, Chubby Checker song (4)
15 Hand gesture (4)
16 ___ Titchmarsh, TV gardener (see picture) (4)
17 Upright part of a staircase between treads (5)
23 ___ Reeves, Hollywood actor (5)
24 Jog with the elbow (5)
25 Arise (3,2)
26 Richard ___, *Watership Down* author (5)
29 ___ Hood, Sherwood outlaw (5)
30 Narrow band of colour on a garment (6)
32 One of a kind (6)
33 Straining vessel (5)
34 Those people (4)
35 Portion of medicine (4)
36 Shout loudly (4)
41 Location of the Taj Mahal (4)
42 Conspiracy (4)
44 Likelihood, as in gambling (4)
45 Shut forcibly (4)
47 UK TV company (inits)(3)
48 Bony facial structure (3)

Jigword

3 letters
AIT
ARM
FOR
MAT
REF
SON
TAN
TEN

4 letters
ATOM
DOOM
HUGE
MARK
RISK
STAR
SURF
THEE

5 letters
ADMIT
CHEER
FELON
HYPER
LURID
READY
REBUT
SINGE
SNOUT
SUITE

6 letters
AWNING
CORRAL
DONNED
DUNDEE
ENSURE
JALOPY
STICKY
WITTER

7 letters
ALARMED
CONDUCT
COOLANT
COURAGE
INHABIT
LIGHTEN
ONESTEP
OTTOMAN
OUTLINE
REACTOR
RUN AWAY
STUDENT
TEATIME

8 letters
BALLYHOO
HARDWARE
STRINGER
THICKSET
WOODWIND

9 letters
ANTIPASTO
~~HALLOWEEN~~
MIDSTREAM
RESTRAINT
WORTHLESS

10 letters
RECIPROCAL

11 letters
BLOODSUCKER
HAUGHTINESS
THISTLEDOWN

Kids' Corner

Colour it

Colour in all the shapes that have a black dot to find out who's taking a night flight.

Two Timer

Two sets of clues to the same answers.

STRAIGHT CLUES

ACROSS

1 Slang term for 'potato' (4)
4 Defensive player in rugby (8)
8 White flower of early spring (8)
9 Liberate (4)
10 Old-fashioned word for 'you' (4)
11 Ripened fruit that has been blown off a tree (8)
14 Time allowed for payment (6)
15 Short burst of rainfall (6)
17 Beyond the end of the visible spectrum (8)
19 Point of land projecting into the sea (4)
20 Pavement's edging stones (4)
21 Hand over (4,4)
22 Cutting both ways (3-5)
23 Subtle hair dye (4)

DOWN

2 Large black leopard (7)
3 Informal name for Australia (4,5)
4 Strong alcoholic liquor (9)
5 Cheeky talk (3)
6 Major blood vessel (5)
7 Cushion used in church (7)
12 Plunged headlong (4-5)
13 Graphic representation of a complex process (4,5)
14 Game played at Lord's (7)
16 Demonstrate the workings of (7)
18 Do without (5)
21 Silence by binding the mouth (3)

CRYPTIC CLUES

ACROSS

1 Vegetable turned up in South Dakota (4)
4 Complete support for footballer (8)
8 Blooming avalanche? (8)
9 Undo reef knot (4)
10 You were in the penthouse (4)
11 Fruit blown off producing unexpected profit (8)
14 Trust Charlie with revolutionary article (6)
15 Revealing bathroom equipment? (6)
17 This radiation could be rare find (8)
19 Cloak, carbon copy (4)
20 Some hillwalker by the roadside (4)
21 Present unintentional revelation (8)
22 Is such a remark doubly sharp? (3-5)
23 Can take time to colour shortly (4)

DOWN

2 Peter at that place cut short by wild beast (7)
3 Defeated and depressed on the other side of the world (4,5)
4 Two elements making strong drink (9)
5 Mouthpiece (3)
6 Eccentric autocrat cut out part of heart (5)
7 It supports one in prayer (7)
12 Dropped sharply, leading feature went into the water (4-5)
13 Tide table (4,5)
14 Sporting jumper (7)
16 Account for old agonising sensation round top of leg (7)
18 Give up fourth turn, say (5)
21 Joke that leaves one speechless (3)

Quiz Wordsearch

Answer the given clues and then find the answers hidden in the grid.

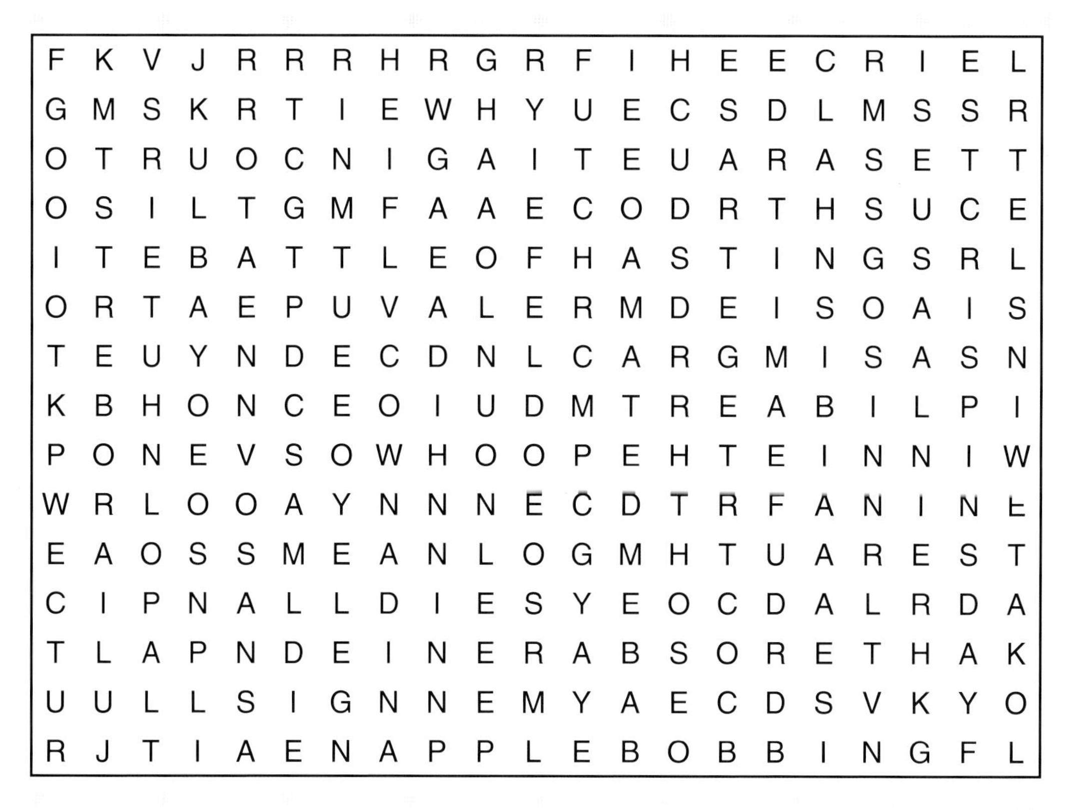

1 14th October 1066 event (6,2,8)

2 25th October (2,8,3)

3 AA Milne's bear first published 14th October 1926 (6,3,4)

4 Birthstone for October (4)

5 Captain Cook's ship in which he discovered New Zealand on 6th October 1769 (9)

6 Famous Henry V victory of 25th October 1415 (9)

7 Fast food chain whose first British outlet opened 1st October 1974 (9)

8 Game played using the teeth (5,7)

9 Horatio _, admiral who defeated the French at Trafalgar 21st October 1805 (6)

10 Orange flower of the daisy family, birth flower for October (9)

11 *Pretty Woman* actress whose birthday is 25th October (5,7)

12 Scottish star of 1990 film *The Hunt for Red October* (4,7)

13 Singer whose album Frank contains the track October Song (3,9)

14 Star of *The Bourne Ultimatum* whose birthday is 8th October (4,5)

15 *Titanic* star whose birthday is 5th October (4,7)

Logic Problem

In Berlin back in the bad old days of the Cold War, Rosenstrasse 23 (or, in English, 23 Rose Street) was a 'safe house' where the British Security Service would keep defectors from behind the Iron Curtain while they were waiting for transport to the UK. From the clues given, can you work out the codename assigned to the Soviet defectors occupying each of the rooms there on the night of January 1st, 1972, the man's real name and his job before he defected?

Clues

1 Yuri Scriabin, codenamed Earwig, had been assigned the room with a number one up from the one where the psychologist was awaiting passage to Britain.

2 Boris Glazunov was a Soviet Navy lieutenant before he decided to flee to the West.

3 The man in room 5 was Oleg Borodin.

4 'Spruce' was the codename assigned to the man in room 3.

5 The defecting KGB officer was in room 2.

6 Bantam, who had been a pilot for the Soviet airline Aeroflot, had the room numbered immediately below that assigned to Kipper.

7 Sergei Rimsky was not the defector who had been given the codename Poodle.

	Bantam	Earwig	Kipper	Poodle	Spruce	Boris Glazunov	Igor Korzakov	Oleg Borodin	Sergei Rimsky	Yuri Scriabin	Airline pilot	Journalist	KGB officer	Naval officer	Psychologist
1															
2															
3															
4															
5															
Airline pilot															
Journalist															
KGB officer															
Naval officer															
Psychologist															
Boris Glazunov															
Igor Korzakov															
Oleg Borodin															
Sergei Rimsky															
Yuri Scriabin															

Room	Codename	Real name	Occupation

Jolly Mixtures

ACROSS
1 DETRAINS
6 SEAT
8 POET
9 ALTER TUB
10 DUST
11 DARTED
13 DYED
15 CORED
17 RAGED
19 FEEL
21 SUREST
24 CASK
26 A MELTING
27 NAME
28 MANE
29 ALERTING

DOWN
2 TUTOR
3 MADE DEN
4 SUNDER
5 TUBED
6 ARTEX
7 EASE DEW
12 GEAR
14 NODE
16 RETINUE
18 RATTERS
20 LINTEL
22 SAINT
23 REITH
25 LANCE

Solutions

Wordsearch

Z	I	T	I	I	C	N	I	K	P	M	U	P	F	L	O	W	E	R	E	W
T	A	B	R	O	K	N	O	C	K	O	N	D	O	O	R	S	I	P	S	M
C	I	N	B	I	S	L	L	I	E	B	S	S	E	K	L	I	O	G	C	O
N	A	W	O	E	C	I	U	M	D	S	A	I	K	A	C	I	E	N	R	T
L	E	U	S	M	V	K	U	O	S	O	E	N	N	U	N	O	T	I	E	N
B	R	H	L	E	E	T	O	K	H	L	O	T	D	T	L	N	L	S	A	A
R	B	E	D	D	S	D	E	R	L	G	E	L	E	A	S	L	U	R	M	H
O	R	E	D	O	R	L	L	A	T	R	L	D	B	T	G	O	C	S	A	P
O	O	R	C	I	E	O	F	A	N	R	H	H	E	E	H	E	C	G	G	W
D	O	A	E	T	P	T	N	I	R	A	E	E	A	D	K	T	O	R	N	F
Y	M	A	O	R	H	S	E	P	T	U	W	A	E	L	M	A	A	S	R	A
K	S	N	L	G	I	P	T	N	A	S	T	T	T	A	L	V	F	E	E	C
A	T	D	I	Z	O	M	B	I	E	R	N	A	S	A	E	O	T	H	Y	E
E	I	N	R	U	M	U	C	S	E	U	T	K	N	Y	I	S	W	L	P	P
R	C	A	T	G	I	B	O	N	A	E	R	Y	A	R	N	S	I	E	E	A
C	K	S	Y	A	D	E	V	H	E	D	N	R	T	O	E	E	R	I	E	I
L	L	P	R	Y	N	S	E	H	E	S	D	U	M	A	I	P	N	T	R	N
E	W	O	R	M	I	O	N	I	F	F	O	C	V	A	L	G	U	S	C	T
I	E	O	D	M	G	O	N	S	S	E	R	D	Y	C	N	A	F	S	R	T
A	E	K	H	U	H	G	I	B	L	A	C	K	C	A	T	F	A	N	G	S
S	H	Y	L	M	T	H	C	T	I	W	V	A	M	P	I	R	E	R	G	O

Number Jig

	6		6	2	5			
	1		7		1			
8	8	1	5	5	3	7		9
1			0		2			8
7	8	8	0		0			3
0		7			4	0	6	0
2		3		6				5
5	5	7	4	4	7			2
5		2		8		9	0	5

Linkword

HEAT, IRON, SOAP, SIDE, FORK, CUBE, BELL **HOPEFUL**

Sudoku

4	2	9	3	5	1	8	6	7
3	6	7	9	4	8	5	2	1
1	8	5	2	6	7	9	3	4
9	1	8	6	7	5	2	4	3
7	4	3	1	9	2	6	8	5
6	5	2	8	3	4	1	7	9
5	3	6	4	8	9	7	1	2
8	9	1	7	2	3	4	5	6
2	7	4	5	1	6	3	9	8

Short Code

R	A	R	E	■	T	I	R	E
■	L	■	T	U	R	N	■	L
C	L	U	E	■	A	N	T	I
L	■	■	R	■	C	■	■	T
A	K	I	N	■	K	I	T	E
N	■	C	A	K	E	■	I	■
K	E	E	L	■	R	U	N	T

L	U	I	C	K
A	T	R	E	N

Brickwork

MAIDEN
AMEND
NAME
MAN
DAMN
NOMAD
DAMSON

Add Up

73

Suko

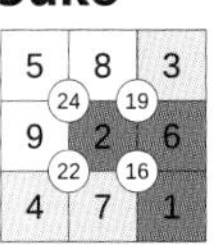

Wordsearch

D	B	E	E	T	L	E	L	E	E
G	K	Y	W	N	O	O	B	A	B
W	S	I	P	P	N	F	S	E	P
A	D	E	P	P	E	I	F	N	E
L	K	I	S	R	U	F	B	S	E
L	H	R	R	O	A	P	U	A	H
A	T	E	I	R	O	H	N	M	S
B	T	U	I	L	E	M	N	A	R
Y	I	G	A	G	L	E	Y	L	N
M	O	T	T	E	R	S	D	L	O

Safecracker

Word Ladder

LOAF, load, lord, cord, card, care, CAKE

Sudoku

4	8	6	1	3	2	5	7	9
3	7	5	6	9	4	2	8	1
2	9	1	7	5	8	4	3	6
5	1	9	8	7	6	3	2	4
6	3	4	2	1	5	7	9	8
8	2	7	3	4	9	1	6	5
9	4	8	5	2	7	6	1	3
1	5	2	9	6	3	8	4	7
7	6	3	4	8	1	9	5	2

Suguru

3	4	1	2	1	4	3
1	2	5	3	5	2	5
4	3	1	2	1	3	1
1	2	4	3	4	5	2
5	3	5	1	2	1	4
1	4	2	3	5	3	2
2	3	1	4	2	4	1

Solutions

Crossword

Pumpkin

Quiz Wordsearch

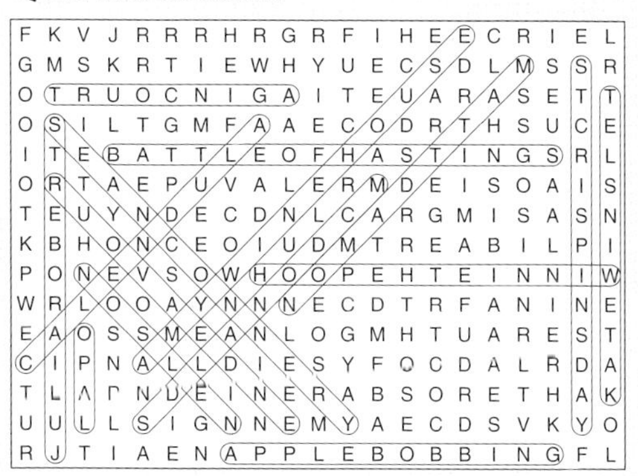

1 BATTLE OF HASTINGS
2 ST CRISPIN'S DAY
3 WINNIE THE POOH
4 OPAL
5 ENDEAVOUR
6 AGINCOURT
7 MCDONALDS
8 APPLE BOBBING
9 NELSON
10 CALENDULA
11 JULIA ROBERTS
12 SEAN CONNERY
13 AMY WINEHOUSE
14 MATT DAMON
15 KATE WINSLET

Jigword

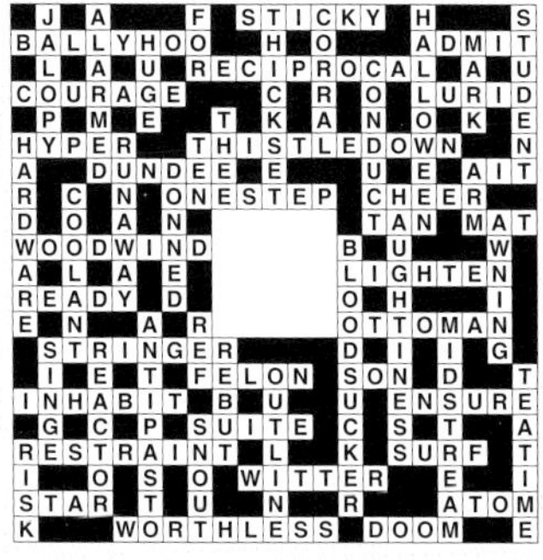

Kids' Corner

Two Timer

ACROSS: 1 Spud 4 Fullback 8 Snowdrop 9 Free 10 Thou 11 Windfall 14 Credit 15 Shower 17 Infrared 19 Cape 20 Kerb 21 Giveaway 22 Two-edged 23 Tint.

DOWN: 2 Panther 3 Down under 4 Firewater 5 Lip 6 Aorta 7 Kneeler 12 Nose-dived 13 Flow chart 14 Cricket 16 Explain 18 Forgo 21 Gag.

Logic Problem

Oleg Borodin was in room 5 (clue 3); he wasn't the naval officer, who was Boris Glazunov (clue 2), or the KGB officer, who was in room 2 (clue 5). Nor can the man in room 5 have been the psychologist (clue 1) or the airline pilot, whose codename was Bantam (clue 6), so Oleg Borodin must have been a journalist. We now know the real names to go with two occupations; from clue 1 we can see Yuri Scriabin wasn't the psychologist, and the same clue tells us that Scriabin's codename was Earwig, so he can't have been the airline pilot, and, by elimination, must have been the KGB officer. He was in room 2, so, from clue 1, the psychologist must have been in room 1. Spruce was in room 3 (clue 4) so the airline pilot, Bantam, must have been in room 4, and, by elimination, Spruce in room 3 must have been Boris Glazunov, the naval officer. Clue 6 now tells us that the man in room 5 was codenamed Kipper, leaving the psychologist in room 1 as Poodle. From clue 7, Poodle wasn't Sergei Rimsky, so he must have been Igor Korzakov, leaving Sergei Rimsky as the man in room 4, the airline pilot codenamed Bantam.

1, 'Poodle', Igor Korzakov, psychologist.
2, 'Earwig', Yuri Scriabin, KGB officer.
3, 'Spruce', Boris Glazunov, naval officer.
4, 'Bantam', Sergei Rimsky, airline pilot.
5, 'Kipper', Oleg Borodin, journalist.

Jolly Mixtures

S	T	R	A	I	N	E	D		E	A	S	T
	R		M		U		E		X		E	
T	O	P	E		R	E	B	U	T	T	A	L
	U		N		S		U		R		W	
S	T	U	D		E		T	R	A	D	E	D
			E	D	D	Y		A			E	
C	R	E	D	O				G	R	A	D	E
	E			N		F	L	E	E			
R	U	S	S	E	T		E		S	A	C	K
	N		T		H		N		T		L	
L	I	G	A	M	E	N	T		A	M	E	N
	T		I		I		I		R		A	
M	E	A	N		R	E	L	A	T	I	N	G

Remember, remember, the 5th of November
The Gunpowder Treason and plot;
I see of no reason why Gunpowder Treason
Should ever be forgot.
Guy Fawkes, Guy Fawkes,
'Twas his intent.
To blow up the King and the Parliament.
Three score barrels of powder below.
Poor old England to overthrow.

Traditional rhyme

Wordsearch

Find all the listed words and phrases associated with November, together with stars celebrating their birthdays this month, hidden in the grid.

ALL SAINT'S DAY
ARMISTICE
BILLY CONNOLLY
BONFIRE NIGHT
CHRYSANTHEMUM
DIWALI
EMMA STONE
FIREWORKS
GERARD BUTLER
GUY FAWKES
MARTINMAS
MATTHEW MCCONAUGHEY
MEG RYAN
REMEMBRANCE DAY
ST ANDREW'S DAY
TOPAZ
VETERAN CAR RUN

SUNDAY
1

MONDAY
2

TUESDAY
3

WEDNESDAY
4

THURSDAY *GUY FAWKES' NIGHT*
5

FRIDAY
6

SATURDAY
7

SUNDAY *REMEMBRANCE SUNDAY*
8

Suko

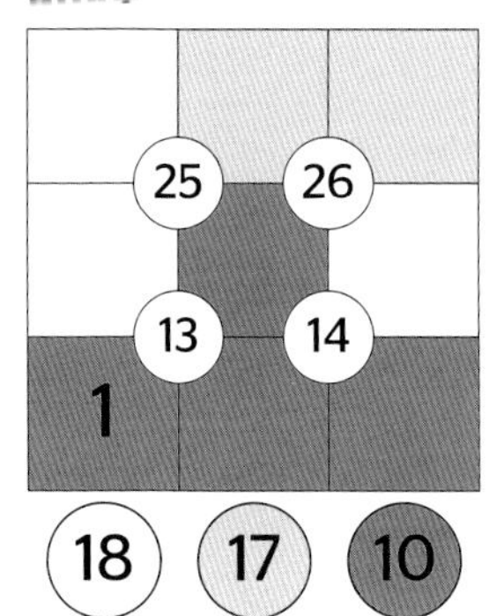

Wordsearch

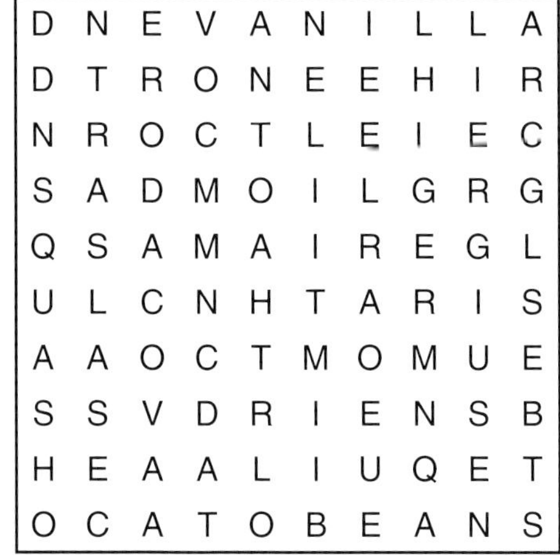

D	N	E	V	A	N	I	L	L	A
D	T	R	O	N	E	E	H	I	R
N	R	O	C	T	L	E	I	E	C
S	A	D	M	O	I	L	G	R	G
Q	S	A	M	A	I	R	E	G	L
U	L	C	N	H	T	A	R	I	S
A	A	O	C	T	M	O	M	U	E
S	S	V	D	R	I	E	N	S	B
H	E	A	A	L	I	U	Q	E	T
O	C	A	T	O	B	E	A	N	S

AVOCADO CREAM SQUASH
BEANS EGGS TACO
BURRITO LIME TEQUILA
CHILLI MOLE TOMATO
CORN SALSA VANILLA

Sudoku

				5				
6	7				2			
	1	5	4		3			
		9			6	3	5	
			3	8				4
5		8		4		7		
	6	4	2		7	5		
9		7				2	6	
	5		9				3	

MONDAY
9

TUESDAY
10

WEDNESDAY
11

THURSDAY
12

FRIDAY
13

SATURDAY
14

SUNDAY
15

MONDAY
16

Number Jig

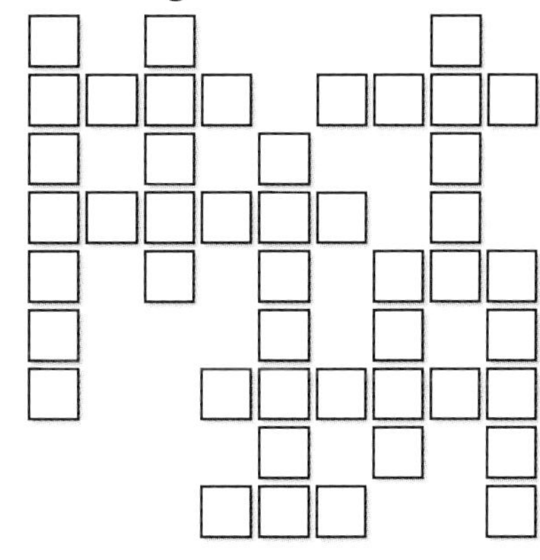

3 digits
324
778

4 digits
1213
2072
3528

5 digits
41052
41544
67322

6 digits
384617
912220

7 digits
2163418
3117127

Short Code

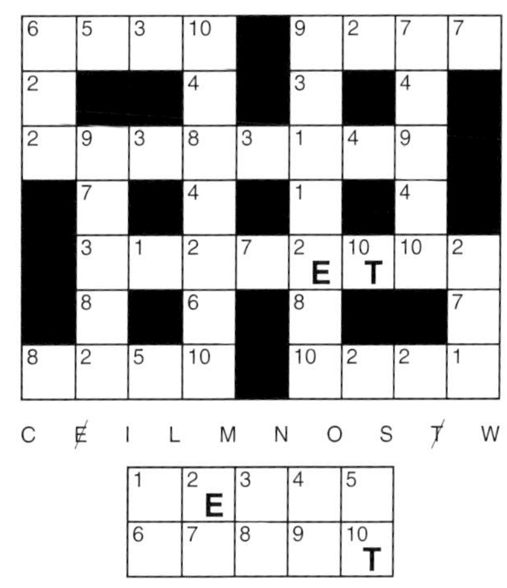

Noughts and Crosses

The numbered squares around the edge of the grid describe the number of crosses in all the vertical, horizontal and diagonal lines connecting with that square.

4	5	4	2	5	2	1
3			0			3
5						3
3					0	4
5		X	0		X	4
3						6
1	3	5	3	7	3	4

Complete the grid so that there is a nought or a cross in every square.

TUESDAY
17

WEDNESDAY
18

THURSDAY
19

FRIDAY
20

SATURDAY
21

SUNDAY
22

MONDAY
23

TUESDAY
24

Linkword

NATURAL					YESTERDAY
TAP					POLISH
ETON					CIRCLE
DOUBLE					LIBERTIES
NEAR					OUT
GAS					STANDARD
ONE					DOWN

Sudoku

							1	3
					8			6
7			4	5	1			
3				4		1	8	
5	2		1	8	6	9		
9				2		5		
	7							
		9		1				
			7	9	4	6		

Brickwork

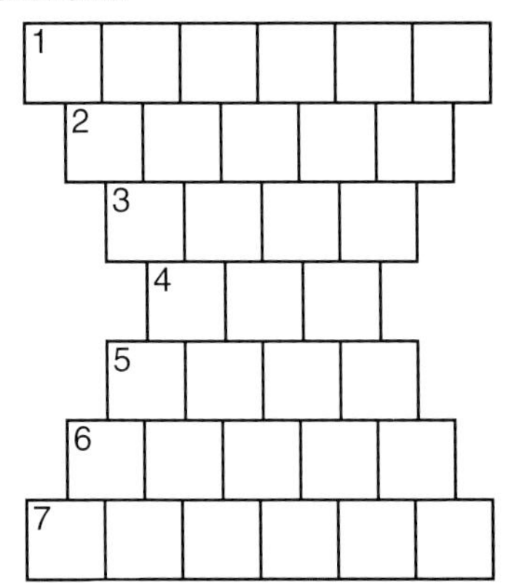

1 Hair tie (6)
2 Batman's friend (5)
3 Ballpoint pen (4)
4 Bone of the torso (3)
5 Feathered friend (4)
6 Plait (5)
7 To do with weddings (6)

WEDNESDAY
25

THURSDAY
26

FRIDAY
27

SATURDAY
28

SUNDAY
29

MONDAY *ST ANDREW'S DAY*
30

NOTES

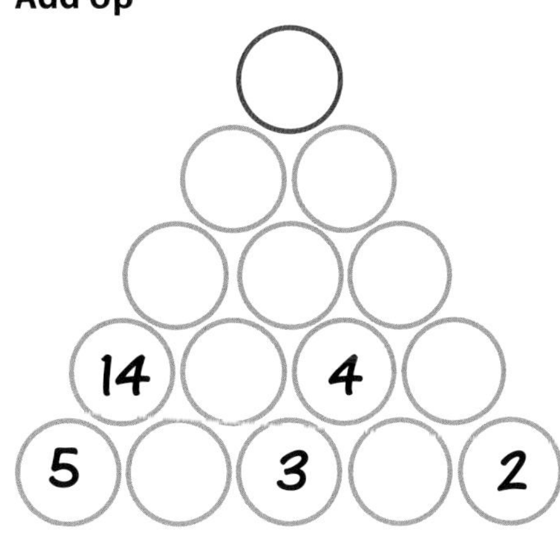

Word Ladder

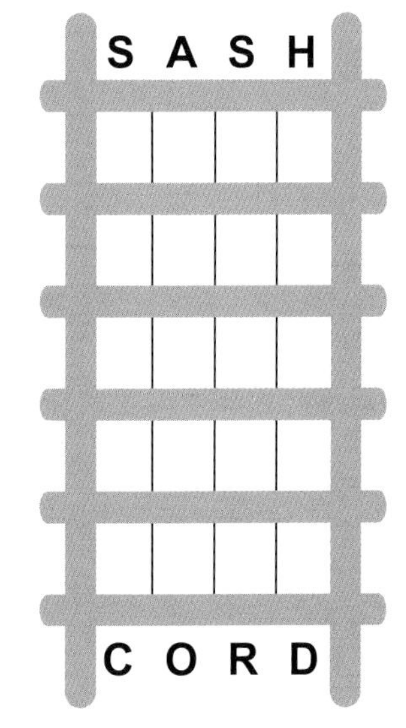

Suguru

			2			
					3	
		4				
		2			1	
		5				

Arroword

Waggly part of a dog
Putting in a row
Apportion
__ candle, firework (see picture)
Snake found in the UK
Sacred hymn or song
Cover (gifts)
Sharpened post
Elderly
Hit (a fly)
Thousand grams
Hit hard
High-priced
Cut (with shears)
Time of life
Be without
Whichever
Large measure of weight
Tousle or crease
Be in possession of
Fruit seeds
Girl's name or part of the eye
Put your name to
Winter weather
Belonging to us
Make tunes with the voice
__ and void, invalid
Revolver, for instance
Price, charge
Solemn appeal or swear-word
Rank, layer
Bright object in the sky
Peaceful
Closely linked (3,2,3)
Animal prized for its fur
Different
Reddish hair-dye
Garbage
Absent, on leave
Crime of disloyalty to one's country
Coax, tempt
In this position
People who extinguish blazes
Telephone, make a call (4,2)
Small unit of length
Swallow noisily
Items for hanging up washing
Safeguard in an electric circuit
Fountain pen fluid
Become unconscious
Allow
Sick, bilious
Be poorly
Karate blow
Limb used for walking
Spring where a flow of water begins
(Had) witnessed
Encountered

Rearrange the letters in the shaded squares to spell out the name of a statesman who was born in November.

Scary Stories

Jim, Fred and Willy are all huge fans of ghost stories. Follow each boy's trail to discover the title of his favourite spine-chiller.

Honeycomb

All the answers are six-letter words. Each answer is entered in a circle around its clue number. The first letter of the answer is entered in the shaded triangle immediately above the clue number. If the clue number is odd, enter the answer in an anti-clockwise direction. If the clue number is even, enter the answer in a clockwise direction.

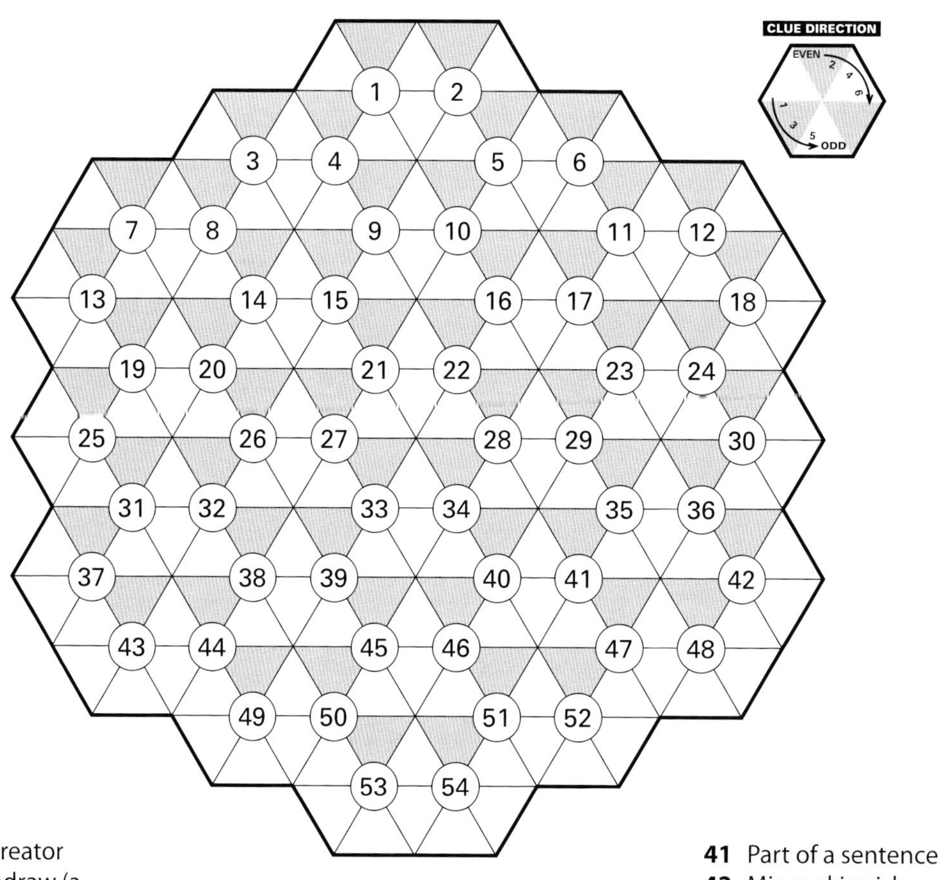

1 Procreator
2 Withdraw (a statement)
3 Declare positively
4 Barbed reply
5 Fondle
6 Estimate the value
7 Novelist
8 Zone
9 Formal headwear (3,3)
10 Say again
11 Time division
12 Use up resources
13 Songbird
14 Root vegetable
15 Vicar's domain
16 Royal residence
17 Plain cotton fabric
18 Czech capital
19 Eastern potentate
20 Waif
21 Register as unemployed (4,2)
22 US gorge
23 Chirping insect
24 African republic
25 Minimum
26 Impose a penalty
27 Armed escort
28 That is to say
29 Film device
30 Towards the rear of a boat
31 Rarely
32 Amusing TV series
33 Stroller
34 Missive
35 Express remorse
36 Begrudge
37 Scaly reptile
38 Road surface material
39 Cooper's product
40 Forceful shove
41 Part of a sentence
42 Minor skirmish
43 Tennis equipment
44 Talisman
45 Judge's white fur
46 Lying face upwards
47 Pub room
48 Financial supporter
49 Province of Northern Ireland
50 Male title
51 Homing bird
52 Hyde Park's city
53 Social standing
54 Exceptional talent

Two for Tea

ACROSS

1 Concerning sound (5)
4 Teenage spots (4)
6 Young fox (3)
7 Scope, range (5)
8 Single entity (4)
9 Disreputable bar or other meeting place (5)
11 Tiny bit of bread (5)
13 Male admirer (4)
14 Pixie-like (5)
16 Alias (inits)(3)
17 *Home and* ___, Australian soap (4)
18 Tree that bears red berries (5)

DOWN

1 ___ Khan, title of a Muslim leader (3)
2 Wreckage (6)
3 Musical arrangement devised for eight players (5)
4 Border, lean upon (4)
5 Place in a grave (6)
9 Desert rodent (6)
10 Time to be in by! (6)
11 Transparent (5)
12 Dockside (4)
15 Convent resident (3)

ACROSS

1 Glowing with heat (3-3)
6 Astonish, surprise (5)
7 Freezing compartment of a fridge (6)
9 House made from snow (5)
12 Drug obtained from poppies (5)
14 One who purchases (5)
16 Dessert or pudding (5)
19 Joined together (6)
21 Baby's tummy-ache (5)
22 South African national park (6)

DOWN

1 Large horned mammal, in short (5)
2 Female rabbit or deer (3)
3 Vehicle available for hire (4)
4 Roald ___, author (4)
5 Office note (4)
8 Senselessly cruel person (5)
10 Famous Barcelona architect (5)
11 Honours system award (inits)(3)
13 Bench or seat in a church (3)
15 Aircraft warning system (5)
16 Unwell (4)
17 French word for 'she' (4)
18 ___ in, eat heartily (4)
20 Tie-on label (3)

Patch of the Day

Place the two smaller squares (they are the right way up) over the larger grid so that no colour appears twice in the same row or column.

Pattern Maker

Can you spot the pattern in this sequence, and work out what comes next from the five options?

Jumbo Codeword

The letters in the phrase box will spell out the name of something that was first ridden in November 1885.

12	14	4	12	3	15	16		1	20	25 A	9	14
14		24			26	20	3	24		5 L		22
11	25	7		16	22	22		5	12	1 P		22
22		19	22	22		25	13	26		25	14	13
23	26	26		14		13	22	14		23		5
16		5	22	4	4		19		22	25	4	22
	8		20	22	25	5	12	3	14		21	
4	25	3	25		5		16		23		18	
	14		13	20	25	3		16	26	10	12	14
	3		12		13	25	7		18		20	
2	25	14	23	24		4	26	26	14		20	
	20		25		6		14		16	15	22	14
	26		16	15	12	4	16	5	22		5	
13	26	17	22		20		15	25	20	16		3
12		26		19	18	4		16		25	12	20
4	25	13		25	4	15		15	12	7		18
25		12	5	5		26	13	22		22	5	7
20		25		4	9	25	24			4		1
7	26	23	15	25		5	22	14	3	16	15	24

~~A~~ B C D E F G H I J K ~~L~~ M N O ~~P~~ Q R S T U V W X Y Z

1 P	2	3	4	5 L	6	7	8	9	10	11	12	13
14	15	16	17	18	19	20	21	22	23	24	25 A	26

7	26	16	26	20	19	12	8	22

Roundabout

Solutions to Radial clues (1 to 24) either start from the outer edge of the circle and read inwards, or start from the inner ring and read outwards to the edge (so they are all five-letter words). Solutions to Circular clues read in either a clockwise or an anti-clockwise direction round the circle.

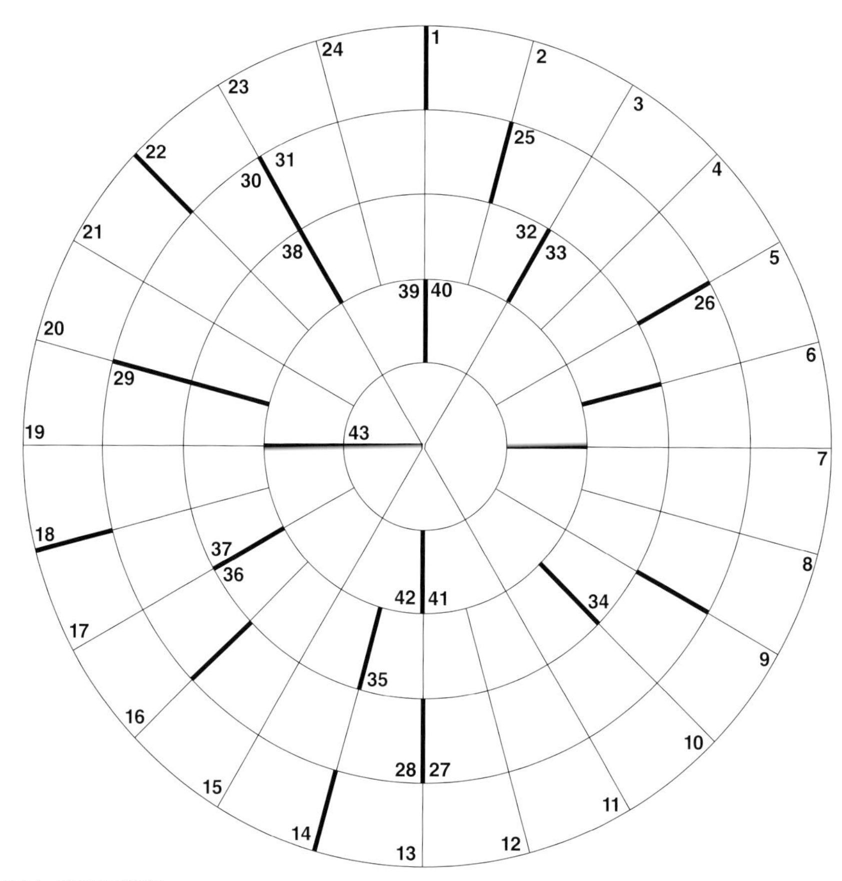

RADIAL: INWARDS

1 Hooded snake
4 Sweeping implement
6 Seraglio
11 Drying cloth
13 Rope fibre
15 Strained
16 Plant with liquorice-flavoured seeds
18 Hang elegantly
19 Jockey
20 Bury
21 Daily reading matter
23 Stadium
24 Ms Bruce, *Antiques Roadshow* presenter

OUTWARDS

2 Fragrance
3 Tooth
5 Paris Underground
7 The sea
8 Plait
9 Farm machine
10 City of Iraq
12 Tenant's contract
14 Spear
17 Surrey racecourse
22 Respond

CIRCULAR: CLOCKWISE

1 Food group
18 Leak
25 Spoil
26 Raja's wife
28 Frozen water
31 Brazilian city
33 Auction item
37 Miserable
40 Fish eggs
42 Serpent
43 Countryside walk

ANTI-CLOCKWISE

17 Chum
24 Lard
27 Painful
29 Press clothes
30 Tin
32 Woodwind instrument
34 Den
35 Cuts wood
36 Tavern
38 Suitable
39 Born as
41 Hearing organ

Logic Problem

Many celebrities are seen on TV these days endorsing a variety of products, and five advertising agencies have recently secured the services of five of the biggest names. From the information given below, can you discover which agency has booked which name, the field in which each is famous, and the product each will be promoting?

Clues

1 The singer, who is neither Aiden Sellars nor Drew Byers, will be in a series of adverts for a department store; Drew Byers, who is also not an actor, has been booked by Pitch, Huckster and Hawke.

2 Keene and Partners are not making an advert with Brandon Sayle, or the one for shampoo; the shampoo advert doesn't star the model.

3 Sparkes are making the coffee advert.

4 Creativation have secured the services of the TV presenter.

5 Guy Hansom will be in the car advert.

6 Ernie Bucks is a footballer.

	Ernie Bucks	Drew Byers	Guy Hansom	Brandon Sayle	Aiden Sellars	Actor	Footballer	Model	Presenter	Singer	Car	Coffee	Department store	Perfume	Shampoo
Creativation															
Future Vision															
Keene and Partners															
Pitch, Huckster and Hawke															
Sparkes															
Car															
Coffee															
Department store															
Perfume															
Shampoo															
Actor															
Footballer															
Model															
Presenter															
Singer															

Agency	Celebrity	Field	Product

Pathfinder

Beginning with the letter E in the shaded square, follow a single path to find 17 words connected with bonfire night. The trail passes through every letter once and may twist up, down and sideways (but never diagonally).

BANGER	GUNPOWDER
BONFIRE	GUY FAWKES
BOOTS	MISTY
BURNING	ROCKET
CHILDREN	ROMAN CANDLE
DISPLAY	SAFETY
EXPLOSION	SCARF
FIREWORK	TORCHES
GLOVES	

C	R	O	T	G	N	A	B	E	R	E
H	E	S	R	E	I	S	P	L	I	X
E	K	R	I	L	D	N	Y	A	F	P
T	C	O	H	D	R	E	B	O	N	L
B	E	S	C	G	R	E	D	W	O	O
U	K	F	Y	U	V	E	S	N	P	S
R	W	A	A	N	O	L	G	U	O	I
N	R	F	M	C	E	G	S	K	N	B
I	A	R	O	A	L	F	A	R	O	O
N	C	T	S	N	D	E	R	E	W	O
G	S	Y	I	M	Y	T	I	F	S	T

Solutions

Wordsearch

P	V	Z	P	O	P	O	S	O	I	L	G	U	Y	F	A	W	K	E	S	M
Y	S	K	O	I	E	P	Y	A	D	S	W	E	R	D	N	A	T	S	U	H
U	A	E	D	L	S	Y	O	I	E	S	K	E	O	N	I	L	T	M	G	F
B	E	D	C	D	H	E	S	U	I	O	T	R	A	E	P	V	E	L	A	N
R	E	I	E	S	O	H	T	E	C	D	L	Y	O	R	G	H	N	L	I	S
K	H	E	O	C	U	G	T	R	N	E	R	A	B	W	T	I	L	L	B	P
S	O	E	C	D	N	U	G	T	R	G	F	A	N	N	E	S	I	E	I	S
L	O	G	H	T	U	A	A	E	E	R	E	N	A	I	A	R	S	O	L	E
B	C	D	A	L	R	N	R	M	R	T	P	S	N	I	I	E	I	A	L	A
B	O	S	O	R	E	O	T	B	H	A	Y	L	N	U	I	G	R	F	Y	N
A	E	N	C	D	S	C	K	V	M	R	R	T	O	R	T	M	I	A	C	E
N	F	L	F	S	R	C	E	O	H	E	S	D	P	A	I	T	I	S	O	H
N	U	E	C	I	D	M	L	C	S	D	M	R	B	S	G	A	O	A	N	B
T	E	I	T	N	R	W	A	R	A	E	S	E	T	U	O	L	I	M	N	T
O	N	E	C	D	A	E	H	Y	R	U	P	I	R	S	T	E	O	N	O	I
P	L	D	A	T	G	H	N	N	E	R	C	F	S	K	O	L	I	I	L	A
A	B	I	E	C	D	T	N	I	T	E	L	R	H	E	S	U	E	T	L	A
Z	I	W	O	N	T	T	E	P	G	R	W	V	A	L	G	S	I	R	Y	M
E	O	A	C	D	N	A	R	T	A	H	E	I	S	H	L	O	U	A	E	A
N	R	L	B	T	I	M	S	E	F	C	T	E	N	O	T	S	A	M	M	E
D	O	I	V	E	T	E	R	A	N	C	A	R	R	U	N	A	P	L	R	G

Suko

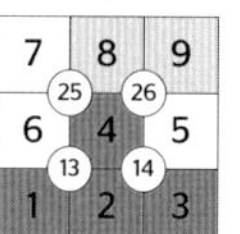

7	8	9
6	4	5
1	2	3

25, 26, 13, 14

Wordsearch

D	N	E	V	A	N	I	L	L	A
D	T	R	O	N	E	E	H	I	R
N	R	O	C	T	L	E	L	E	C
S	A	D	M	O	I	L	G	R	G
Q	S	A	M	A	I	R	E	G	L
U	L	C	N	H	T	A	R	I	S
A	A	O	C	T	M	O	M	U	E
S	S	V	D	R	I	E	N	S	B
H	E	A	A	L	I	U	Q	E	T
O	C	A	T	O	B	E	A	N	S

Sudoku

4	9	2	6	5	1	8	7	3
6	7	3	8	9	2	1	4	5
8	1	5	4	7	3	6	9	2
1	4	9	7	2	6	3	5	8
7	2	6	3	8	5	9	1	4
5	3	8	1	4	9	7	2	6
3	6	4	2	1	7	5	8	9
9	8	7	5	3	4	2	6	1
2	5	1	9	6	8	4	3	7

Number Jig

2		4					6	
1	2	1	3		2	0	7	2
6		5		3			3	
3	8	4	6	1	7		2	
4		4		1		3	2	4
1				7		5		1
8			9	1	2	2	2	0
				2		8		5
			7	7	8			2

Short Code

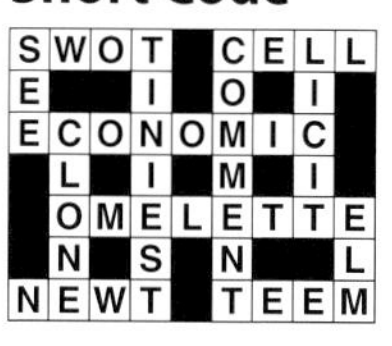

S	W	O	T		C	E	L	L
E			I		O		I	
E	C	O	N	O	M	I	C	
	L		I		M		I	
	O	M	E	L	E	T	T	E
	N		S		N			L
N	E	W	T		T	E	E	M

M	E	O	I	W
S	L	N	C	T

Noughts and Crosses

4	5	4	2	5	2	1
3	X	X	0	0	0	3
5	0	X	0	0	0	3
3	X	0	0	X	0	4
5	0	X	0	X	X	4
3	0	0	X	X	X	6
1	3	5	3	7	3	4

Linkword

BORN, SHOE, CROP, TAKE, MISS, LAMP, STEP **RECEIPT**

Sudoku

2	8	5	6	7	9	4	1	3
4	9	1	2	3	8	7	5	6
7	3	6	4	5	1	2	9	8
3	6	7	9	4	5	1	8	2
5	2	4	1	8	6	9	3	7
9	1	8	3	2	7	5	6	4
1	7	2	5	6	3	8	4	9
6	4	9	8	1	2	3	7	5
8	5	3	7	9	4	6	2	1

Brickwork

RIBBON
ROBIN
BIRO
RIB
BIRD
BRAID
BRIDAL

Add Up

65

Word Ladder

SASH, cash, cast, cart, card, curd, CORD

Suguru

1	3	4	2	1	2	1
4	2	1	3	4	3	4
1	3	4	5	1	5	1
2	5	1	3	2	4	3
1	3	2	4	5	1	2
2	4	5	3	2	3	4
1	3	2	1	4	1	2

Arroword

Winston Churchill

Kids' Corner

Jim - The Headless Horseman
Fred - The Screaming Skull
Willy - The Ghost of the Mad Monk

Honeycomb

1 Parent 2 Recant 3 Assert 4 Retort 5 Caress 6 Assess 7 Author 8 Sector 9 Top hat 10 Repeat 11 Second 12 Expend 13 Thrush 14 Carrot 15 Parish 16 Palace 17 Calico 18 Prague 19 Sultan 20 Orphan 21 Sign on 22 Canyon 23 Cicada 24 Uganda 25 Lowest 26 Punish 27 Gunman 28 Namely 29 Camera 30 Astern 31 Seldom 32 Sitcom 33 Ambler 34 Letter 35 Repent 36 Resent 37 Lizard 38 Tarmac 39 Barrel 40 Thrust 41 Phrase 42 Scrape 43 Racket 44 Amulet 45 Ermine 46 Supine 47 Saloon 48 Patron 49 Ulster 50 Mister 51 Pigeon 52 London 53 Status 54 Genius.

Two for Tea

R	E	D	H	O	T		D		M
H		O			A	M	A	Z	E
I	C	E	B	O	X		H		M
N			R		I	G	L	O	O
O	P	I	U	M		A		B	
	E		T		B	U	Y	E	R
S	W	E	E	T		D			A
I		L		U	N	I	T	E	D
C	O	L	I	C			A		A
K		E		K	R	U	G	E	R

Patch of the Day

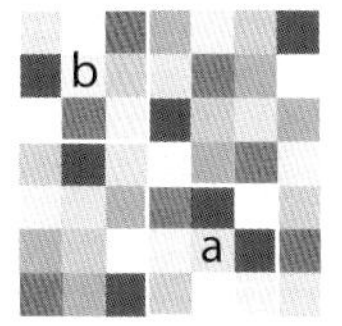

Pattern Maker

Panel 4. With each progression, the dice changes colour in rainbow order, with the number of dots representing the letters in the name of the previous colour. Blue (5).

Jumbo Codeword

P	F	G	S	L	V	M	K	W	X	J	I	D
N	H	T	Z	U	B	R	Q	E	C	Y	A	O

Motorbike

Roundabout

RADIAL: 1 Cobra 2 Aroma 3 Molar 4 Broom 5 Metro 6 Harem 7 Briny 8 Braid 9 Baler 10 Basra 11 Towel 12 Lease 13 Sisal 14 Lance 15 Tense 16 Anise 17 Epsom 18 Drape 19 Rider 20 Inter 21 Paper 22 React 23 Arena 24 Fiona.

CIRCULAR: 1 Carbohydrates 17 Mate 18 Drip 24 Fat 25 Mar 26 Rani 27 Sore 28 Ice 29 Iron 30 Can 31 Rio 32 Oboe 33 Lot 34 Lair 35 Saws 36 Inn 37 Sad 38 Apt 39 Née 40 Roe 41 Ear 42 Asp 43 Ramble.

Logic Problem

The celebrity in the department store advert is neither Aiden Sellars nor Drew Byers (clue 1), and as it is the singer (also clue 1), it is not footballer Ernie Bucks (clue 6) or Guy Hansom, who is in the car advert (clue 5), so it must be Brandon Sayle. He has not been booked by Keene and Partners (clue 2), Pitch, Huckster and Hawke, who have got Drew Byers (clue 1), Sparkes, who are making the coffee advert (clue 3), or Creativation, who have the presenter in their advert (clue 4), so it must be Future Vision. We know that Pitch, Huckster and Hawke have not booked the singer or presenter, nor the footballer Ernie Bucks. As Drew Byers is not an actor (clue 1), she must be the model. Therefore she is not advertising the department store, the coffee or the car. The model is not endorsing the shampoo (clue 2), so Drew Byers must be in Pitch, Huckster and Hawke's perfume advert. Keene and Partners are not making the shampoo advert (clue 2), so must be making the car advert starring Guy Hansom. By elimination, the shampoo advert must have been the Creativation one starring the TV presenter. This is not Ernie Bucks, the footballer, so by elimination it must be Aiden Sellars. Therefore Ernie Bucks must be in Sparkes' coffee advert, and Keene and Partners' star Guy Hansom must be the actor.

Creativation, Aiden Sellars, presenter, shampoo. Future Vision, Brandon Sayle, singer, department store. Keene and Partners, Guy Hansom, actor, car. Pitch, Huckster and Hawke, Drew Byers, model, perfume. Sparkes, Ernie Bucks, footballer, coffee.

Pathfinder

C	R	O	T	G	N	A	B	E	R	E
H	E	S	R	E	I	S	P	L	I	X
E	K	R	I	L	D	N	Y	A	F	P
T	C	O	H	D	R	E	B	O	N	L
B	E	S	C	G	R	E	D	W	O	O
U	K	F	Y	U	V	E	S	N	P	S
R	W	A	A	N	O	L	G	U	O	I
N	R	F	M	C	E	G	S	K	N	B
I	A	R	O	A	L	F	A	R	O	O
N	C	T	S	N	D	E	R	E	W	O
G	S	Y	I	M	Y	T	I	F	S	T

December

'Twas the night before Christmas, when all through the house
Not a creature was stirring, not even a mouse.
The stockings were hung by the chimney with care,
In hopes that St Nicholas soon would be there.

Clement Clarke Moore

Wordsearch

X R Q B I R T H O F C H R I S T B B B U T
U S E T I V N I B L O U O L P S A M X F B
O U L K U M A L F K O A N A P U D D I N G
F S L E C S I O P A A W R N U G E G L R J
G E A N Q A A S S A M T H G I N D I M S I
O J A O S U R M M E Y I Y E C I O J E R N
O O B S E N E C T H V L L A R P E A T O G
D L A A T E D E A S L O N Y Y P S E R D L
W W A E R I I T N O I U L T J O Y P A E E
I O L S P P N T H S A R I P N H N M D E B
L R F E K E N O R H S N H S R S A V I Y E
L B A V E C E S O E A P G C D E I N T D L
L C M I R N R M E I E R E Y R S S I I R L
E E A T U I E E T H E K U E I E V E O A S
A O G S N M G S T E S L I T C I H N N C E
A Y I E P O I R T N E I O N T H W T A T Y
D L R F O R E I G T I R W A D M S T A R E
V E O R H C N L I D N W N D K N I R D F K
E R C C E G T D N O I T A R O C E D A E R
N S H L S M E O C H A R I T Y O U S E A U
T S A N T A C L A U S C A R O L G N S R T

Find all the listed words associated with Christmas.

ADVENT
BIRTH OF CHRIST
CARD
CAROL
CHARITY
CHRISTIANITY
CRACKER
DECORATION
DINNER
DRINK
FAMILY
FATHER CHRISTMAS
FEAST

FESTIVE SEASON
GIFT
GOOD WISHES
GOODWILL
HOLLY
HOME
INVITE
JESUS
JINGLE BELLS
JOY
KINDNESS
LOVE
MAGI

MERRY
MIDNIGHT MASS
MINCE PIE
NATIVITY
NOEL
PARTY HAT
PEACE
PRESENT
PUDDING
QUEEN'S SPEECH
REJOICE
SANTA CLAUS
SCROOGE

SEASON'S GREETINGS
SHOPPING
STAR
TRADITION
TREE
TURKEY
VISITOR
WASSAIL
WINTER
XMAS
YULETIDE

TUESDAY
1

WEDNESDAY
2

THURSDAY
3

FRIDAY
4

SATURDAY
5

SUNDAY
6

MONDAY
7

TUESDAY
8

Suko

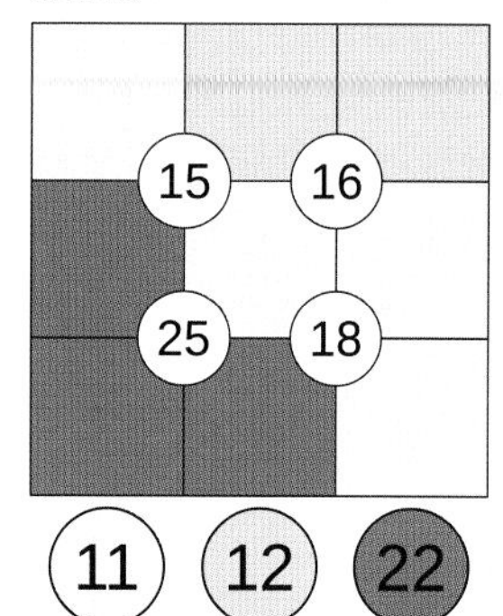

Wordsearch

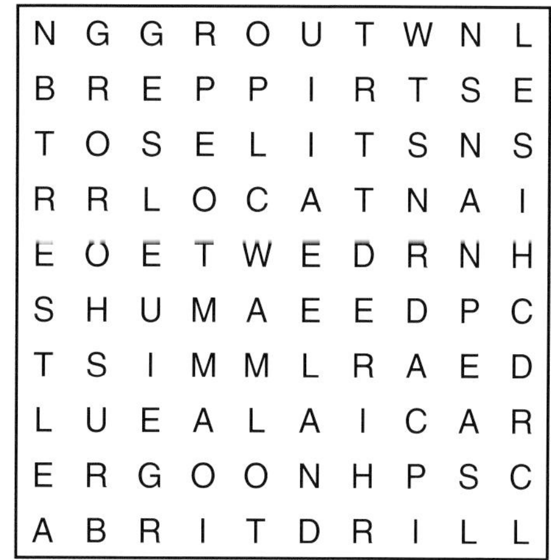

N	G	G	R	O	U	T	W	N	L
B	R	E	P	P	I	R	T	S	E
T	O	S	E	L	I	T	S	N	S
R	R	L	O	C	A	T	N	A	I
E	O	E	T	W	E	D	R	N	H
S	H	U	M	A	E	E	D	P	C
T	S	I	M	M	L	R	A	E	D
L	U	E	A	L	A	I	C	A	R
E	R	G	O	O	N	H	P	S	C
A	B	R	I	T	D	R	I	L	L

BOLT
BRUSH
CHISEL
DRILL
GROUT
HAMMER
PAD
PAINT
ROLLER
SCREW
STEAMER
LADDER
STRIPPER
TILES
TRESTLE

Sudoku

	1	3						
						4	5	1
2		7		4				3
5			7		9		6	
	9				2		7	
8			1		6		9	
7		2		1				6
						7	1	8
	3	5						

WEDNESDAY
9

THURSDAY
10

FRIDAY
11

SATURDAY
12

SUNDAY
13

MONDAY
14

TUESDAY
15

WEDNESDAY
16

Number Jig

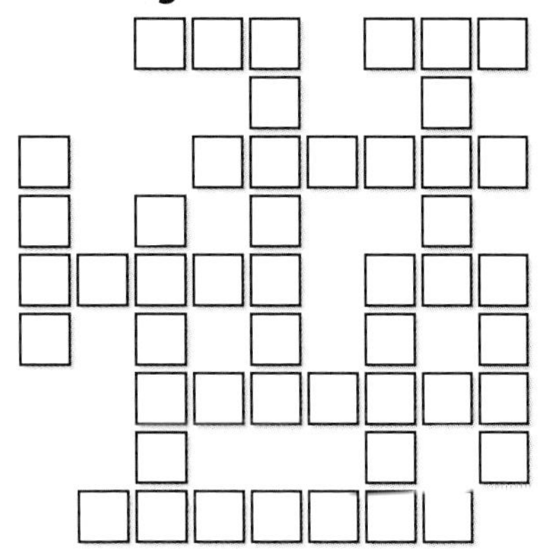

3 digits	5 digits	7 digits
344	35566	3176167
663	94731	3827460
990	96664	6573500

4 digits	6 digits
4302	272466
6094	871668

Short Code

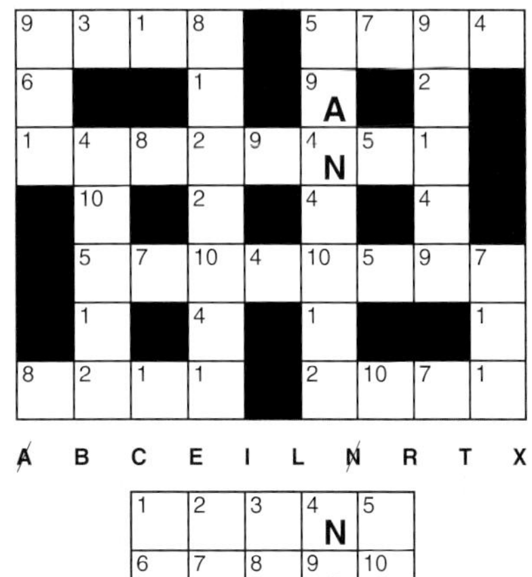

The Great Divide

Divide up the grid into four equally sized, equally shaped parts, each containing five different coloured symbols.

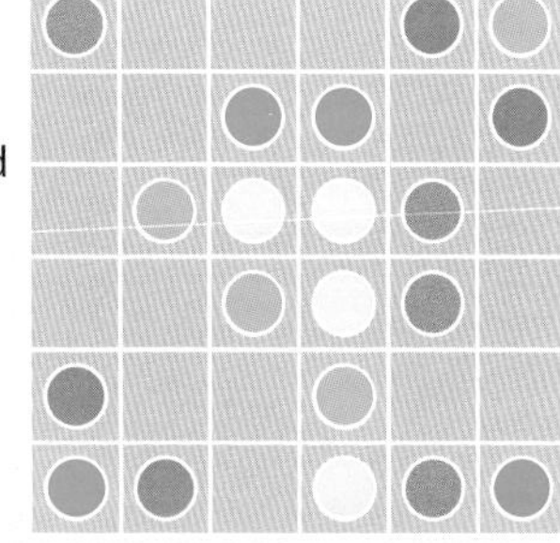

THURSDAY
17

FRIDAY
18

SATURDAY
19

SUNDAY
20

MONDAY
21

TUESDAY
22

WEDNESDAY
23

THURSDAY
24

Linkword

TAKE					CHAIR
FIDDLER					APPLE
BLUE					BOOTS
THAT'S					SAID
KARATE					SUEY
GOLD					HOUR
HARD					SHORT

Sudoku

				1				
	3							4
					4		7	9
				8				6
6			2		9	4		
		8		4		9	2	5
				9	2			
		7			1		9	
	1	6	4		3			2

Brickwork

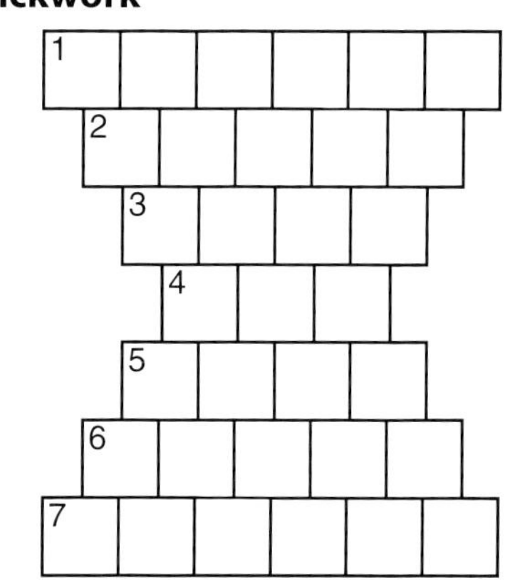

1 Respond (6)
2 Accustoms to solid food (5)
3 Beautiful white bird (4)
4 Past tense of 'is' (3)
5 Hit (a fly) (4)
6 Use uneconomically (5)
7 Covered with perspiration (6)

FRIDAY *CHRISTMAS DAY (BANK HOLIDAY)*

25

SATURDAY *BOXING DAY (BANK HOLIDAY)*

26

SUNDAY

27

MONDAY

28

TUESDAY

29

WEDNESDAY

30

THURSDAY *NEW YEAR'S EVE*

31

Add Up

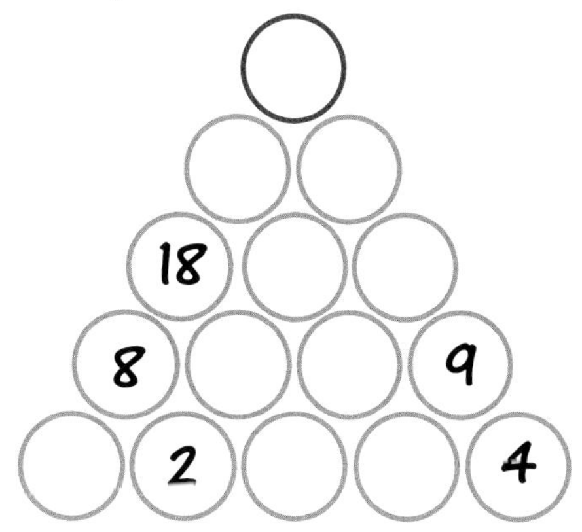

Word Ladder

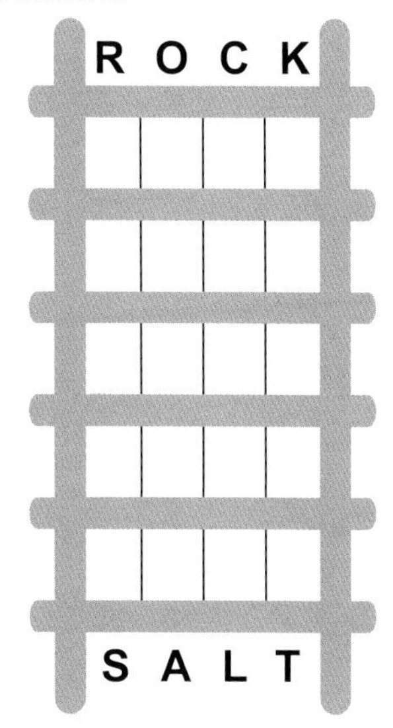

Suguru

					2	1
	3					
4		5		2		
					5	
		5				

Crossword

Take the letters in the shaded squares to spell out the name of a location which holds a swimming race in December.

ACROSS

1 That lady's (4)
6 Place of residence (4)
8 Free, on the loose (2,5)
9 Item worn on the head (3)
11 Painting (3)
13 Tailed heavenly body (5)
16 Tidy and clean feathers with the beak (5)
18 In a higher position (5)
19 Sound of a hen (5)
20 Burn with boiling water (5)
21 Happening, occurrence (5)
22 Prolonged dull pain (4)
25 Highly strung, twitchy (4)
27 Versatile vegetarian foodstuff (4)
28 Item used in a stage play (4)
29 State of owing money (4)
31 Sharp pull (4)
34 Fundamental principle (5)
37 Safety ___, automatic tap in a boiler (5)
38 Quiz-show team or wooden board (5)
39 Shred (cheese) (5)
40 ___ rehearsal, practice in costume (5)
43 ___ Lowe, model (5)
46 Alien spacecraft (inits)(3)
49 Big ___, Westminster landmark (3)
50 Admit (defeat) (7)
51 Ship's floor (4)
52 Hollow cylinder (4)

DOWN

2 Sound which bounces back (4)
3 Glut (4)
4 One of Santa's helpers? (see picture) (3)
5 ___ wolf, give a false alarm (3)
6 Detect sound (4)
7 Final chess move (4)
10 Lie in wait to attack (6)
12 Gift in return for a deed or service (6)
13 Chocolate-flavoured milky drink (5)
14 ___ after, resemble (4)
15 Roadworks marker (4)
16 Troublesome or annoying person or thing (4)
17 Big Ears' friend (5)
23 Humid and muggy (5)
24 Explode violently (volcano) (5)
25 Having nothing inside (5)
26 Sound of pain or anguish (5)
29 Plunged head first into water (5)
30 Faith (6)
32 Parent's sister (6)
33 ___ Osbourne, Ozzy's pop-star daughter (5)
34 Entreats (4)
35 Drench (4)
36 Travelled quickly (4)
41 Regulation (4)
42 Item of clothing for the foot (4)
44 Assist (in a crime) (4)
45 Of a nose, short and turned up (4)
47 Old coaching house (3)
48 Sopping (3)

Picture Pair

How quickly can you spot the two identical pictures?

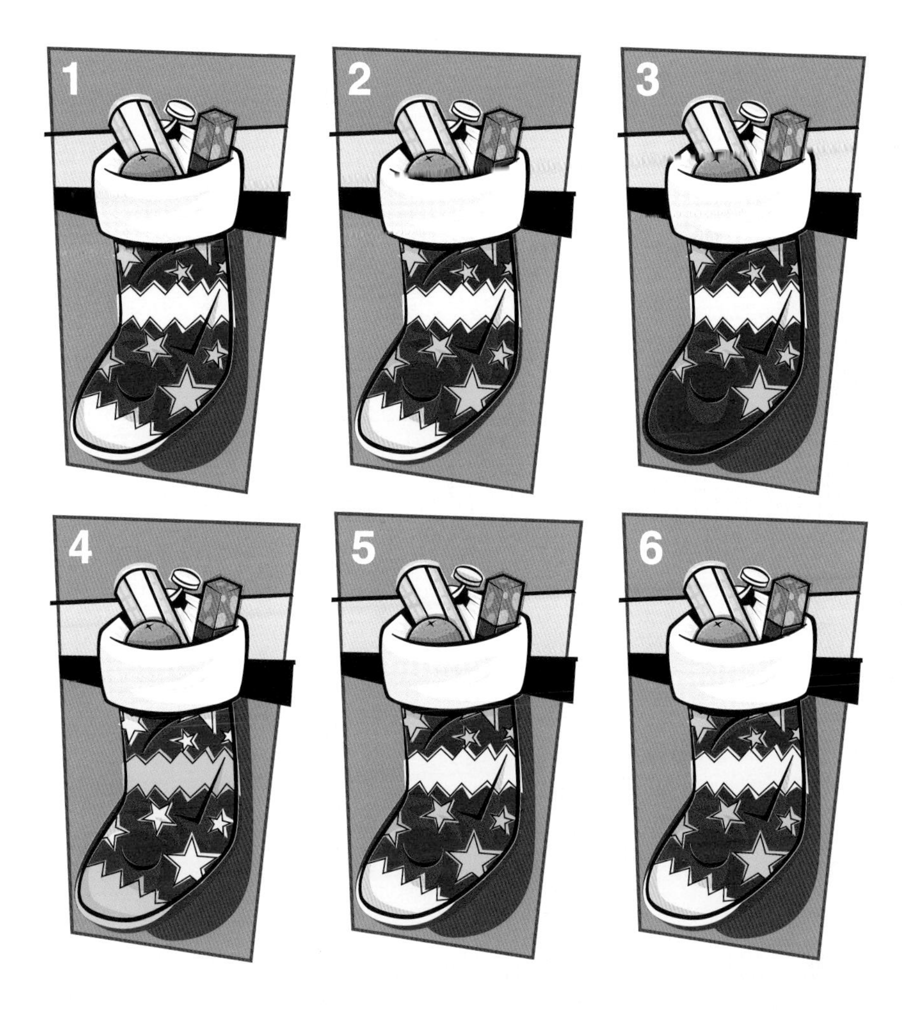

Quiz Wordsearch

Answer the given clues and then find the answers hidden in the grid.

F	K	V	J	S	R	E	G	D	O	R	N	O	T	N	A	L	A	X	Q	G
P	C	O	R	O	N	A	T	I	O	N	S	T	R	E	E	T	D	E	L	H
E	S	E	C	M	Y	L	G	T	I	E	P	S	M	B	F	I	V	E	L	H
U	S	E	A	C	I	A	U	B	E	L	G	I	O	S	K	I	E	E	P	J
H	U	H	N	E	C	R	D	L	R	S	R	N	I	E	R	E	N	S	E	U
I	W	L	T	E	Q	G	N	G	M	A	D	F	A	E	C	M	T	R	H	D
S	U	I	T	U	L	E	P	A	N	E	D	V	A	L	N	I	C	R	E	I
I	S	N	O	O	A	L	T	D	R	I	Y	P	E	C	L	M	A	R	G	D
N	M	I	I	S	A	K	A	F	H	C	X	E	I	O	U	O	L	T	R	E
N	S	B	E	A	B	H	L	Y	I	L	I	O	P	T	S	T	E	W	O	N
E	E	O	C	T	A	A	R	F	D	A	N	S	B	I	T	N	N	E	S	C
L	O	R	G	R	M	H	T	U	A	O	R	E	S	N	I	A	D	Y	S	H
E	O	C	T	D	A	L	R	T	P	N	O	I	E	U	A	P	A	B	S	O
R	E	T	H	Y	A	W	R	O	T	O	M	W	U	L	S	I	R	G	N	M
A	E	C	D	S	K	V	T	Y	R	A	B	A	N	K	S	O	R	T	I	A

1 Actor who played Achilles in *Troy* whose birthday is 18th December (4,4)

2 Actor who played the solicitor in *May to December* (5,7)

3 Birthstone for December (9)

4 Christmas show (9)

5 Christmas-card bird (5)

6 Comedienne with her own sitcom (7,4)

7 December almanac (6,8)

8 Feast of St Stephen (6,3)

9 Group who sang *Last Christmas* (4)

10 Major road for fast traffic, the first in Britain opened 5th December 1958 (8)

11 Swedish inventor of dynamite who has a range of prizes awarded in December named after him (6,5)

12 TV soap that began on 10th December 1960 (10,6)

13 US director of *Annie Hall* whose birthday is 1st December (5,5)

14 US model turned TV personality whose birthday is 4th December (4,5)

15 Veteran British actress who is a DBE whose birthday is 9th December (4,5)

16 Yellow flower, birth flower for December (9)

Logic Problem

Five young cousins, all on a family holiday in the West Country, spent a day beachcombing on the sands below Littleberry Point, and all made interesting finds – though their parents were mostly horrified. From the clues below, can you work out the age of each of the cousins, where he or she made her find and what it was?

Clues

1. The child who found a shell buried in the sand – dating from 1942 and which was designed for use in an anti-aircraft gun – was older than Jason, who found a treasure chest full of jewellery which the police think may be related to a series of burglaries.
2. Lucy, at 11, is older than her sister Emily.
3. The cousin who found the old deck chair with a label saying 'Do Not Remove From RMS Titanic' is not the oldest of the five.
4. The 7-year-old who found the dead whale isn't David, who is the younger brother of Paul, who made his discovery in a rock pool.
5. The child who found something under the pier was older than the one who found something equally interesting – but not the deck-chair – under a rock.
6. The cousin who found something floating about in the surf was 10 years old.

	5	7	10	11	13	Buried in sand	In rock pool	In surf	Under pier	Under rock	Dead whale	Deck chair	Rugby ball	Shell	Treasure chest
David															
Emily															
Jason															
Lucy															
Paul															
Dead whale															
Deck chair															
Rugby ball															
Shell															
Treasure chest															
Buried in sand															
In rock pool															
In surf															
Under pier															
Under rock															

Name	Age	Location	Item

Jolly Mixtures

ACROSS

1 THRASHES
6 SIRE
8 ERGO
9 AMORTISE
10 BART
11 EVELYN
13 DOER
15 HER US
17 OARED
19 HOLA
21 ESCORT
24 LOST
26 OTHER GAS
27 HATE
28 FORM
29 ENTIRETY

DOWN

2 ARGUE
3 RESPECT
4 SEARED
5 ETHOS
6 ARIES
7 ALL REST
12 VALE
14 FORE
16 MOTHERS
18 HOLD PIN
20 HEADER
22 REMUS
23 SETAE
25 STOAT

Solutions

Wordsearch

X	R	Q	B	I	R	T	H	O	F	C	H	R	I	S	T	B	B	B	U	T
U	S	E	T	I	V	N	I	B	L	O	U	O	L	P	S	A	M	X	F	B
O	U	L	K	U	M	A	L	F	K	O	A	N	A	P	U	D	D	I	N	G
F	S	L	E	C	S	I	O	P	A	A	W	R	N	U	G	E	G	L	R	J
G	E	A	N	Q	A	A	S	S	A	M	T	H	G	I	N	D	I	M	S	I
O	J	A	O	S	U	R	M	M	E	Y	I	Y	E	C	I	O	J	E	R	N
O	O	B	S	E	N	E	C	T	H	V	L	L	A	R	P	E	A	T	O	G
D	L	A	A	T	E	D	E	A	S	L	O	N	Y	Y	P	S	E	R	D	L
W	W	A	E	R	I	I	T	N	O	I	U	L	T	J	O	Y	P	A	E	E
I	O	L	S	P	P	N	T	H	S	A	R	I	P	N	H	N	M	D	E	B
L	R	F	E	K	E	N	O	R	H	S	N	H	S	R	S	A	V	I	Y	E
L	B	A	V	E	C	E	S	O	E	A	P	G	C	D	E	I	N	T	D	L
L	C	M	I	R	N	R	M	E	I	E	R	E	Y	R	S	S	I	I	R	L
E	E	A	T	U	I	E	E	T	H	E	K	U	E	I	E	V	E	O	A	S
A	O	G	S	N	M	G	S	T	E	S	L	I	T	C	I	H	N	N	C	E
A	Y	I	E	P	O	I	R	T	N	E	I	O	N	T	H	W	T	A	T	Y
D	L	R	F	O	R	E	I	G	T	I	R	W	A	D	M	S	T	A	R	E
V	E	O	R	H	C	N	L	I	D	N	W	N	D	K	N	I	R	D	F	K
E	R	C	C	E	G	T	D	N	O	I	T	A	R	O	C	E	D	A	E	R
N	S	H	L	S	M	E	O	C	H	A	R	I	T	Y	O	U	S	E	A	U
T	S	A	N	T	A	C	L	A	U	S	C	A	R	O	L	G	N	S	R	T

Number Jig

		6	6	3		9	9	0
				1			6	
6			2	7	2	4	6	6
0		8		6			6	
9	4	7	3	1		3	4	4
4		1		6		5		3
		6	5	7	3	5	0	0
		6				6		2
	3	8	2	7	4	6	0	

Linkword

WING, CRAB, MOON, THAT, CHOP, RUSH, SELL **GANACHE**

Sudoku

7	6	4	9	1	5	2	3	8
1	3	9	7	2	8	5	6	4
8	2	5	3	6	4	1	7	9
4	9	2	5	8	7	3	1	6
6	5	1	2	3	9	4	8	7
3	7	8	1	4	6	9	2	5
5	8	3	6	9	2	7	4	1
2	4	7	8	5	1	6	9	3
9	1	6	4	7	3	8	5	2

Short Code

A	B	E	T		C	L	A	N
X			E		A		R	
E	N	T	R	A	N	C	E	
	I		R		N		N	
	C	L	I	N	I	C	A	L
	E		N		E			E
T	R	E	E		R	I	L	E

E	R	B	N	C
X	L	T	A	I

Brickwork

ANSWER
WEANS
SWAN
WAS
SWAT
WASTE
SWEATY

Add Up

86

Suko

2	4	8
6	3	1
7	9	5

15, 16, 25, 18

Wordsearch

N	G	G	R	O	U	T	W	N	L
B	R	E	P	P	I	R	T	S	E
T	O	S	E	L	I	T	S	N	S
R	R	L	O	C	A	T	N	A	I
E	O	E	T	W	E	D	R	N	H
S	H	U	M	A	E	E	D	P	C
T	S	I	M	M	L	R	A	E	D
L	U	E	A	L	A	I	C	A	R
E	R	G	O	O	N	H	P	S	C
A	B	R	I	T	D	R	I	L	L

Word Ladder

ROCK, mock, mack, mask, mast, malt, SALT

Suguru

3	2	3	4	1	5	3
1	4	1	5	3	2	1
2	3	2	4	1	5	4
4	1	5	3	2	3	2
2	3	2	4	1	5	1
5	4	1	3	2	4	2
1	2	5	4	1	3	1

The Great Divide

Sudoku

4	1	3	5	9	8	6	2	7
9	6	8	2	7	3	4	5	1
2	5	7	6	4	1	9	8	3
5	2	1	7	3	9	8	6	4
3	9	6	4	8	2	1	7	5
8	7	4	1	5	6	3	9	2
7	8	2	9	1	4	5	3	6
6	4	9	3	2	5	7	1	8
1	3	5	8	6	7	2	4	9

Crossword

The Serpentine

Picture Pair

Pictures 1 & 6

Quiz Wordsearch

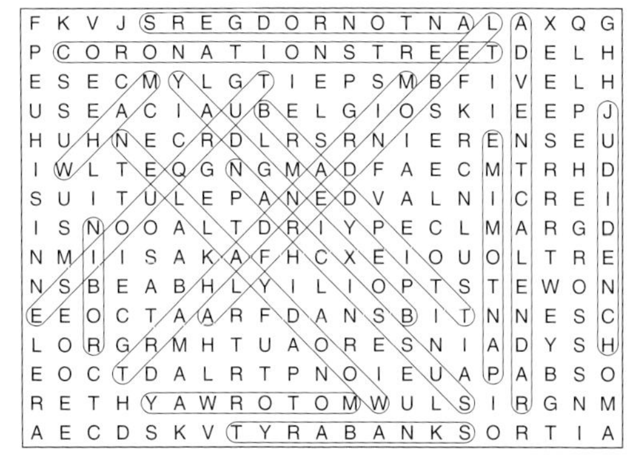

1 BRAD PITT
2 ANTON RODGERS
3 TURQUOISE
4 PANTOMIME
5 ROBIN
6 MIRANDA HART
7 ADVENT CALENDAR
8 BOXING DAY
9 WHAM
10 MOTORWAY
11 ALFRED NOBEL
12 *CORONATION STREET*
13 WOODY ALLEN
14 TYRA BANKS
15 JUDI DENCH
16 NARCISSUS

Logic Problem

The oldest of the cousins, who is 13, can't be Jason (clue 1), Lucy, who is 11, or Emily (clue 2), nor David (clue 4), so must be Paul, who found something in the rock pool (clue 4). It wasn't the deck chair (clue 3), the treasure chest, which was found by Jason (clue 1), the dead whale, found by the 7-year-old (clue 4), or the shell, which was buried in the sand (clue 1), so Paul must have found a rugby ball. We know that the 7-year-old who found the dead whale wasn't Jason, Lucy or Paul, and clue 4 rules out David, so the 7-year-old must be Emily. The 5-year-old didn't find anything buried in the sand (clue 1), under the pier (clue 5) or in the surf, where the 10-year old's item was found (clue 6); we know it was 13-year-old Paul who made a find in the rock pool, so the 5-year-old must have found an item under a rock. From his or her age, the find can't have been the dead whale, and we know it wasn't the shell or the rugby ball; nor was it the deck chair (clue 5), so it must have been the treasure chest, and the 5-year-old is therefore Jason. By elimination, the 10-year-old who found something in the surf must have been David. The child who found the shell buried in the sand can't have been Emily, who found the whale, so must have been Lucy, aged 11. This leaves Emily finding her dead whale under the pier, and David's find in the surf as the deck chair.

David, 10, in surf, deck chair. Emily, 7, under pier, dead whale. Jason, 5, under rock, treasure chest. Lucy, 11, buried in sand, shell. Paul, 13, in rock pool, rugby ball.

Jolly Mixtures

H	A	R	S	H	E	S	T	■	R	I	S	E
■	U	■	C	■	R	■	H	■	A	■	T	■
O	G	R	E	■	A	T	O	M	I	S	E	R
■	E	■	P	■	S	■	S	■	S	■	L	■
B	R	A	T	■	E	■	E	V	E	N	L	Y
■	■	■	R	O	D	E	■	E	■	■	A	■
U	S	H	E	R	■	■	■	A	D	O	R	E
■	M	■	■	F	■	H	A	L	O	■	■	■
C	O	R	S	E	T	■	D	■	L	O	T	S
■	T	■	E	■	E	■	H	■	P	■	O	■
S	H	O	R	T	A	G	E	■	H	E	A	T
■	E	■	U	■	S	■	R	■	I	■	S	■
F	R	O	M	■	E	T	E	R	N	I	T	Y